S0-BNR-123

Good
day
Every
day

Follow us on social media!

Tag us and use #piccadillyinc in your posts
for a chance to win monthly prizes!

This edition published by Piccadilly (USA) Inc.

Piccadilly (USA) Inc.
12702 Via Cortina, Suite 203
Del Mar, CA 92014
USA

10 9 8 7 6 5 4 3 2 1

Printed in China

ISBN-13: 978-1-62009-366-5

ENJOY TODAY

TODAY IS A GOOD DAY TO:

DATE: 2 / 06 / 20

MON TUE WED THU FRI SAT SUN

(THU marked)

TODAY I AM FEELING:

headache + tired

THE WEATHER TODAY WAS:

(snow marked)

TODAY I AM GRATEFUL FOR:

nailing most of rehearsal

MY FAVORITE PART OF TODAY WAS:

my health

(arrows drawn: "nailing" → "my health" box; "my health" → "rehearsal" box)

TO-DO LIST

WHAT I ATE TODAY:

BREAKFAST	LUNCH	DINNER
		chicken wild rice soup

NOTES:

thinking about how yesterday Will said as we were discussing our views of sex (in response to me saying it gratified me to feel sexy + appreciated) that he hoped I could feel that way all the time, that's how he feels

DON'T FORGET!

* read Maslow

DAILY INSPIRATION:

"You must be the change you wish to see in the world."

-GANDHI

PRODUCTIVITY SCORE FOR TODAY:

1 2 3 4 5 6 7 8 9 10

(7 marked)

ENJOY TODAY

TODAY IS A GOOD DAY TO:

be a Friday ;)

DATE: 2 / 7 / 20

MON TUE WED THU FRI SAT SUN

TODAY I AM FEELING:

THE WEATHER TODAY WAS:

TODAY I AM GRATEFUL FOR:

TO-DO LIST

MY FAVORITE PART OF TODAY WAS:

WHAT I ATE TODAY:

BREAKFAST	LUNCH	DINNER

NOTES:

DON'T FORGET!

work on short story

DAILY INSPIRATION:

"Life is really simple, but we insist on making it complicated."

—CONFUCIUS

PRODUCTIVITY SCORE FOR TODAY:

1 2 3 4 5 6 7 8 9 10

ENJOY TODAY

TODAY IS A GOOD DAY TO:

DATE: ____/____/____

MON TUE WED THU FRI SAT SUN

TODAY I AM FEELING:

THE WEATHER TODAY WAS:

TODAY I AM GRATEFUL FOR:

TO-DO LIST

MY FAVORITE PART OF TODAY WAS:

WHAT I ATE TODAY:

BREAKFAST	LUNCH	DINNER

NOTES:

DON'T FORGET!

DAILY INSPIRATION:

"It is by acts, and not by ideas that people live."

-ANATOLE FRANCE

PRODUCTIVITY SCORE FOR TODAY:

1 2 3 4 5 6 7 8 9 10

ENJOY TODAY

TODAY IS A GOOD DAY TO:

DATE: ______ / ______ / ______

MON TUE WED THU FRI SAT SUN

TODAY I AM FEELING:

THE WEATHER TODAY WAS:

TODAY I AM GRATEFUL FOR:

TO-DO LIST

MY FAVORITE PART OF TODAY WAS:

WHAT I ATE TODAY:

BREAKFAST	LUNCH	DINNER

NOTES:

DON'T FORGET!

DAILY INSPIRATION:

"Happy he who possesses this double power of meditation and inspiration, which is genius!"

-VICTOR HUGO

PRODUCTIVITY SCORE FOR TODAY:

1 2 3 4 5 6 7 8 9 10

ENJOY TODAY

TODAY IS A GOOD DAY TO:

DATE: ____ / ____ / ____

MON TUE WED THU FRI SAT SUN

TODAY I AM FEELING:

THE WEATHER TODAY WAS:

TODAY I AM GRATEFUL FOR:

TO-DO LIST

MY FAVORITE PART OF TODAY WAS:

WHAT I ATE TODAY:

BREAKFAST	LUNCH	DINNER

NOTES:

DON'T FORGET!

DAILY INSPIRATION:

"Variety is the source of all our pleasures, and pleasure ceases to be so when it becomes a habit."

–ÉVARISTE PARNY

PRODUCTIVITY SCORE FOR TODAY:

1 2 3 4 5 6 7 8 9 10

ENJOY TODAY

TODAY IS A GOOD DAY TO:

DATE: ____/____/____

MON TUE WED THU FRI SAT SUN

TODAY I AM FEELING:

THE WEATHER TODAY WAS:

TODAY I AM GRATEFUL FOR:

TO-DO LIST

MY FAVORITE PART OF TODAY WAS:

WHAT I ATE TODAY:

BREAKFAST	LUNCH	DINNER

NOTES:

DON'T FORGET!

DAILY INSPIRATION:

"Genius is one percent inspiration, ninety-nine percent perspiration."

-THOMAS EDISON

PRODUCTIVITY SCORE FOR TODAY:

1 2 3 4 5 6 7 8 9 10

ENJOY TODAY

TODAY IS A GOOD DAY TO:

DATE: ____/____/____

MON TUE WED THU FRI SAT SUN

TODAY I AM FEELING:

THE WEATHER TODAY WAS:

TODAY I AM GRATEFUL FOR:

TO-DO LIST

MY FAVORITE PART OF TODAY WAS:

WHAT I ATE TODAY:

BREAKFAST	LUNCH	DINNER

NOTES:

DON'T FORGET!

DAILY INSPIRATION:

"Beware of over-great pleasure in being popular or even beloved."

-MARGARET FULLER

PRODUCTIVITY SCORE FOR TODAY:

1 2 3 4 5 6 7 8 9 10

ENJOY TODAY

TODAY IS A GOOD DAY TO:

DATE: ____ / ____ / ____

MON TUE WED THU FRI SAT SUN

TODAY I AM FEELING:

THE WEATHER TODAY WAS:

TODAY I AM GRATEFUL FOR:

TO-DO LIST

MY FAVORITE PART OF TODAY WAS:

WHAT I ATE TODAY:

BREAKFAST	LUNCH	DINNER

NOTES:

DON'T FORGET!

DAILY INSPIRATION:

"As a well-spent day brings happy sleep, so life well used brings happy death."

-LEONARDO DA VINCI

PRODUCTIVITY SCORE FOR TODAY:

1 2 3 4 5 6 7 8 9 10

ENJOY TODAY

TODAY IS A GOOD DAY TO:

DATE: ____ / ____ / ____

MON TUE WED THU FRI SAT SUN

TODAY I AM FEELING:

THE WEATHER TODAY WAS:

TODAY I AM GRATEFUL FOR:

TO-DO LIST

MY FAVORITE PART OF TODAY WAS:

WHAT I ATE TODAY:

BREAKFAST	LUNCH	DINNER

NOTES:

DON'T FORGET!

DAILY INSPIRATION:

"Dost thou love life? Then do not squander time; for that is the stuff life is made of."

-BENJAMIN FRANKLIN

PRODUCTIVITY SCORE FOR TODAY:

1 2 3 4 5 6 7 8 9 10

ENJOY TODAY

TODAY IS A GOOD DAY TO:

DATE: ______ / ______ / ______

MON TUE WED THU FRI SAT SUN

TODAY I AM FEELING:

THE WEATHER TODAY WAS:

TODAY I AM GRATEFUL FOR:

TO-DO LIST

MY FAVORITE PART OF TODAY WAS:

WHAT I ATE TODAY:

BREAKFAST	LUNCH	DINNER

NOTES:

DON'T FORGET!

DAILY INSPIRATION:

"What a strange illusion it is to suppose that beauty is goodness!"

-LEO TOLSTOY

PRODUCTIVITY SCORE FOR TODAY:

1 2 3 4 5 6 7 8 9 10

ENJOY TODAY

TODAY IS A GOOD DAY TO:

DATE: ____/____/____

MON TUE WED THU FRI SAT SUN

TODAY I AM FEELING:

THE WEATHER TODAY WAS:

TODAY I AM GRATEFUL FOR:

TO-DO LIST

MY FAVORITE PART OF TODAY WAS:

WHAT I ATE TODAY:

BREAKFAST	LUNCH	DINNER

NOTES:

DON'T FORGET!

DAILY INSPIRATION:

"A breath of our inspiration
Is the life of each generation."

-ARTHUR O'SHAUGHNESSY

PRODUCTIVITY SCORE FOR TODAY:

1 2 3 4 5 6 7 8 9 10

ENJOY TODAY

TODAY IS A GOOD DAY TO:

DATE: ____ / ____ / ____

MON TUE WED THU FRI SAT SUN

TODAY I AM FEELING:

THE WEATHER TODAY WAS:

TODAY I AM GRATEFUL FOR:

TO-DO LIST

MY FAVORITE PART OF TODAY WAS:

WHAT I ATE TODAY:

BREAKFAST	LUNCH	DINNER

NOTES:

DON'T FORGET!

DAILY INSPIRATION:

"To be is to think
and to be thinkable.
To live is to continue thinking
and to remember having done so."

-SAMUEL BUTLER

PRODUCTIVITY SCORE FOR TODAY:

1 2 3 4 5 6 7 8 9 10

ENJOY TODAY

TODAY IS A GOOD DAY TO:

DATE: ____/____/____

MON TUE WED THU FRI SAT SUN

TODAY I AM FEELING:

THE WEATHER TODAY WAS:

TODAY I AM GRATEFUL FOR:

TO-DO LIST

MY FAVORITE PART OF TODAY WAS:

WHAT I ATE TODAY:

BREAKFAST	LUNCH	DINNER

NOTES:

DON'T FORGET!

DAILY INSPIRATION:

"The important thing is this: to be ready at any moment to sacrifice what you are for what you could become."

–CHARLES DUBOIS

PRODUCTIVITY SCORE FOR TODAY:

1 2 3 4 5 6 7 8 9 10

Enjoy Today

TODAY IS A GOOD DAY TO:

DATE: ______ / ______ / ______

MON TUE WED THU FRI SAT SUN

TODAY I AM FEELING:

THE WEATHER TODAY WAS:

TODAY I AM GRATEFUL FOR:

TO-DO LIST

MY FAVORITE PART OF TODAY WAS:

WHAT I ATE TODAY:

BREAKFAST	LUNCH	DINNER

NOTES:

DON'T FORGET!

DAILY INSPIRATION:

"An early morning walk is a blessing for the whole day."

-HENRY DAVID THOREAU

PRODUCTIVITY SCORE FOR TODAY:

1 2 3 4 5 6 7 8 9 10

ENJOY TODAY

TODAY IS A GOOD DAY TO:

DATE: ______ / ______ / ______

MON TUE WED THU FRI SAT SUN

TODAY I AM FEELING:

THE WEATHER TODAY WAS:

TODAY I AM GRATEFUL FOR:

TO-DO LIST

MY FAVORITE PART OF TODAY WAS:

WHAT I ATE TODAY:

BREAKFAST	LUNCH	DINNER

NOTES:

DON'T FORGET!

DAILY INSPIRATION:

"Not how long, but how well you have lived is the main thing."

-LUCIUS ANNAEUS SENECA

PRODUCTIVITY SCORE FOR TODAY:

1 2 3 4 5 6 7 8 9 10

ENJOY TODAY

TODAY IS A GOOD DAY TO:

DATE: ____ / ____ / ____

MON TUE WED THU FRI SAT SUN

TODAY I AM FEELING:

THE WEATHER TODAY WAS:

TODAY I AM GRATEFUL FOR:

TO-DO LIST

MY FAVORITE PART OF TODAY WAS:

WHAT I ATE TODAY:

BREAKFAST	LUNCH	DINNER

NOTES:

DON'T FORGET!

DAILY INSPIRATION:

"The winds and waves are always on the side of the ablest navigators."

-EDWARD GIBBON

PRODUCTIVITY SCORE FOR TODAY:

1 2 3 4 5 6 7 8 9 10

ENJOY TODAY

TODAY IS A GOOD DAY TO:

DATE: ____ / ____ / ____

MON TUE WED THU FRI SAT SUN

TODAY I AM FEELING:

THE WEATHER TODAY WAS:

TODAY I AM GRATEFUL FOR:

TO-DO LIST

MY FAVORITE PART OF TODAY WAS:

WHAT I ATE TODAY:

BREAKFAST	LUNCH	DINNER

NOTES:

DON'T FORGET!

DAILY INSPIRATION:

"The difference between a good man and a bad one is the choice of the cause."

-WILLIAM JAMES

PRODUCTIVITY SCORE FOR TODAY:

1 2 3 4 5 6 7 8 9 10

ENJOY TODAY

TODAY IS A GOOD DAY TO:

DATE: ______ / ______ / ______

MON TUE WED THU FRI SAT SUN

TODAY I AM FEELING:

THE WEATHER TODAY WAS:

TODAY I AM GRATEFUL FOR:

TO-DO LIST

MY FAVORITE PART OF TODAY WAS:

WHAT I ATE TODAY:

BREAKFAST	LUNCH	DINNER

NOTES:

DON'T FORGET!

DAILY INSPIRATION:

"Very little is needed to make a happy life."

-MARCUS AURELIUS

PRODUCTIVITY SCORE FOR TODAY:

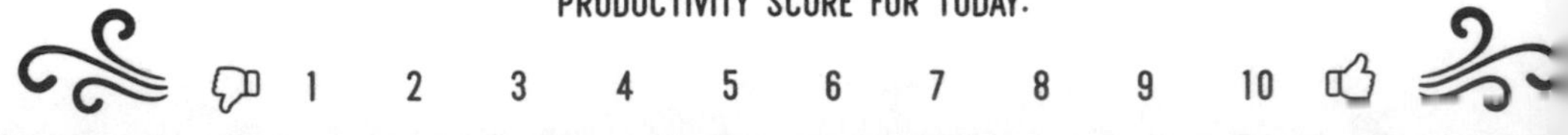

ENJOY TODAY

TODAY IS A GOOD DAY TO:

DATE: ______ /______ /______

MON TUE WED THU FRI SAT SUN

TODAY I AM FEELING:

THE WEATHER TODAY WAS:

TODAY I AM GRATEFUL FOR:

TO-DO LIST

MY FAVORITE PART OF TODAY WAS:

WHAT I ATE TODAY:

BREAKFAST	LUNCH	DINNER

NOTES:

DON'T FORGET!

DAILY INSPIRATION:

"The better part of one's life consists of his friendships."

–ABRAHAM LINCOLN

PRODUCTIVITY SCORE FOR TODAY:

1 2 3 4 5 6 7 8 9 10

ENJOY TODAY

TODAY IS A GOOD DAY TO:

DATE: ____ / ____ / ____

MON TUE WED THU FRI SAT SUN

TODAY I AM FEELING:

THE WEATHER TODAY WAS:

TODAY I AM GRATEFUL FOR:

TO-DO LIST

MY FAVORITE PART OF TODAY WAS:

WHAT I ATE TODAY:

BREAKFAST	LUNCH	DINNER

NOTES:

DON'T FORGET!

DAILY INSPIRATION:

"Lord, grant that I may always desire more than I can accomplish."

-MICHELANGELO

PRODUCTIVITY SCORE FOR TODAY:

1 2 3 4 5 6 7 8 9 10

ENJOY TODAY

TODAY IS A GOOD DAY TO:

DATE: ____ / ____ / ____

MON TUE WED THU FRI SAT SUN

TODAY I AM FEELING:

THE WEATHER TODAY WAS:

TODAY I AM GRATEFUL FOR:

TO-DO LIST

MY FAVORITE PART OF TODAY WAS:

WHAT I ATE TODAY:

BREAKFAST	LUNCH	DINNER

NOTES:

DON'T FORGET!

DAILY INSPIRATION:

"Life can only be understood backwards; but it must be lived forwards."

-SØREN KIERKEGAARD

PRODUCTIVITY SCORE FOR TODAY:

1 2 3 4 5 6 7 8 9 10

Enjoy Today

TODAY IS A GOOD DAY TO:

DATE: ____ / ____ / ____

MON TUE WED THU FRI SAT SUN

TODAY I AM FEELING:

THE WEATHER TODAY WAS:

TODAY I AM GRATEFUL FOR:

TO-DO LIST

MY FAVORITE PART OF TODAY WAS:

WHAT I ATE TODAY:

BREAKFAST	LUNCH	DINNER

NOTES:

DON'T FORGET!

DAILY INSPIRATION:

"Everything one invents is true, you may be perfectly sure of that."

-GUSTAVE FLAUBERT

PRODUCTIVITY SCORE FOR TODAY:

1 2 3 4 5 6 7 8 9 10

ENJOY TODAY

TODAY IS A GOOD DAY TO:

DATE: ______ /______ /______

MON TUE WED THU FRI SAT SUN

TODAY I AM FEELING:

THE WEATHER TODAY WAS:

TODAY I AM GRATEFUL FOR:

TO-DO LIST

MY FAVORITE PART OF TODAY WAS:

WHAT I ATE TODAY:

BREAKFAST	LUNCH	DINNER

NOTES:

DON'T FORGET!

DAILY INSPIRATION:

"Do not take life too seriously—you will never get out of it alive."

-ELBERT HUBBARD

PRODUCTIVITY SCORE FOR TODAY:

1 2 3 4 5 6 7 8 9 10

Enjoy Today

TODAY IS A GOOD DAY TO:

DATE: ____ / ____ / ____

MON TUE WED THU FRI SAT SUN

TODAY I AM FEELING:

THE WEATHER TODAY WAS:

TODAY I AM GRATEFUL FOR:

TO-DO LIST

MY FAVORITE PART OF TODAY WAS:

WHAT I ATE TODAY:

BREAKFAST	LUNCH	DINNER

NOTES:

DON'T FORGET!

DAILY INSPIRATION:

"Keep love in your heart. A life without it is like a sunless garden when the flowers are dead."

-OSCAR WILDE

PRODUCTIVITY SCORE FOR TODAY:

1 2 3 4 5 6 7 8 9 10

ENJOY TODAY

TODAY IS A GOOD DAY TO:

DATE: ____/____/____

MON TUE WED THU FRI SAT SUN

TODAY I AM FEELING:

THE WEATHER TODAY WAS:

TODAY I AM GRATEFUL FOR:

TO-DO LIST

MY FAVORITE PART OF TODAY WAS:

WHAT I ATE TODAY:

BREAKFAST	LUNCH	DINNER

NOTES:

DON'T FORGET!

DAILY INSPIRATION:

"Those who bring sunshine into the lives of others cannot keep it from themselves."

-JAMES M. BARRIE

PRODUCTIVITY SCORE FOR TODAY:

1 2 3 4 5 6 7 8 9 10

ENJOY TODAY

TODAY IS A GOOD DAY TO:

DATE: ______ / ______ / ______

MON TUE WED THU FRI SAT SUN

TODAY I AM FEELING:

THE WEATHER TODAY WAS:

TODAY I AM GRATEFUL FOR:

TO-DO LIST

MY FAVORITE PART OF TODAY WAS:

WHAT I ATE TODAY:

BREAKFAST	LUNCH	DINNER

NOTES:

DON'T FORGET!

DAILY INSPIRATION:

"'Tis better to have loved and lost;
Than never to have loved at all."

-ALFRED TENNYSON

PRODUCTIVITY SCORE FOR TODAY:

1 2 3 4 5 6 7 8 9 10

Enjoy Today

TODAY IS A GOOD DAY TO:

DATE: ____/____/____

MON TUE WED THU FRI SAT SUN

TODAY I AM FEELING:

THE WEATHER TODAY WAS:

TODAY I AM GRATEFUL FOR:

TO-DO LIST

MY FAVORITE PART OF TODAY WAS:

WHAT I ATE TODAY:

BREAKFAST	LUNCH	DINNER

NOTES:

DON'T FORGET!

DAILY INSPIRATION:

"Loquacity storms the ear, but modesty wins the heart."

–THOMAS FULLER

PRODUCTIVITY SCORE FOR TODAY:

1 2 3 4 5 6 7 8 9 10

ENJOY TODAY

TODAY IS A GOOD DAY TO:

DATE: ____/____/____

MON TUE WED THU FRI SAT SUN

TODAY I AM FEELING:

THE WEATHER TODAY WAS:

TODAY I AM GRATEFUL FOR:

TO-DO LIST

MY FAVORITE PART OF TODAY WAS:

WHAT I ATE TODAY:

BREAKFAST	LUNCH	DINNER

NOTES:

DON'T FORGET!

DAILY INSPIRATION:

"Listen widely to remove your doubts and be careful when speaking about the rest and your mistakes will be few."

-CONFUCIUS

PRODUCTIVITY SCORE FOR TODAY:

1 2 3 4 5 6 7 8 9 10

ENJOY TODAY

TODAY IS A GOOD DAY TO:

DATE: ____ / ____ / ____

MON TUE WED THU FRI SAT SUN

TODAY I AM FEELING:

THE WEATHER TODAY WAS:

TODAY I AM GRATEFUL FOR:

TO-DO LIST

MY FAVORITE PART OF TODAY WAS:

WHAT I ATE TODAY:

BREAKFAST	LUNCH	DINNER

NOTES:

DON'T FORGET!

DAILY INSPIRATION:

"We should gain more by letting the world see what we are than by trying to seem what we are not."

-FRANÇOIS DE LA ROCHEFOUCAULD

PRODUCTIVITY SCORE FOR TODAY:

1 2 3 4 5 6 7 8 9 10

Enjoy Today

TODAY IS A GOOD DAY TO:

DATE: ____/____/____

MON TUE WED THU FRI SAT SUN

TODAY I AM FEELING:

THE WEATHER TODAY WAS:

TODAY I AM GRATEFUL FOR:

TO-DO LIST

MY FAVORITE PART OF TODAY WAS:

WHAT I ATE TODAY:

BREAKFAST	LUNCH	DINNER

NOTES:

DON'T FORGET!

DAILY INSPIRATION:

"Time will explain it all."

-EURIPIDES

PRODUCTIVITY SCORE FOR TODAY:

1 2 3 4 5 6 7 8 9 10

ENJOY TODAY

TODAY IS A GOOD DAY TO:

DATE: ______ / ______ / ______

MON TUE WED THU FRI SAT SUN

TODAY I AM FEELING:

THE WEATHER TODAY WAS:

TODAY I AM GRATEFUL FOR:

TO-DO LIST

MY FAVORITE PART OF TODAY WAS:

WHAT I ATE TODAY:

BREAKFAST	LUNCH	DINNER

NOTES:

DON'T FORGET!

DAILY INSPIRATION:

"None is a fool always, everyone sometimes."

-GEORGE HERBERT

PRODUCTIVITY SCORE FOR TODAY:

1 2 3 4 5 6 7 8 9 10

ENJOY TODAY

TODAY IS A GOOD DAY TO:

DATE: _____ / _____ / _____

MON TUE WED THU FRI SAT SUN

TODAY I AM FEELING:

THE WEATHER TODAY WAS:

TODAY I AM GRATEFUL FOR:

TO-DO LIST

MY FAVORITE PART OF TODAY WAS:

WHAT I ATE TODAY:

BREAKFAST	LUNCH	DINNER

NOTES:

DON'T FORGET!

DAILY INSPIRATION:

"But better die than live mechanically a life that is a repetition of repetitions."

-D. H. LAWRENCE

PRODUCTIVITY SCORE FOR TODAY:

1 2 3 4 5 6 7 8 9 10

ENJOY TODAY

TODAY IS A GOOD DAY TO:

DATE: ____ / ____ / ____

MON TUE WED THU FRI SAT SUN

TODAY I AM FEELING:

THE WEATHER TODAY WAS:

TODAY I AM GRATEFUL FOR:

TO-DO LIST

MY FAVORITE PART OF TODAY WAS:

WHAT I ATE TODAY:

BREAKFAST	LUNCH	DINNER

NOTES:

DON'T FORGET!

DAILY INSPIRATION:

"If we are to use women for the same things as the men, we must also teach them the same things."

-SOCRATES

PRODUCTIVITY SCORE FOR TODAY:

1 2 3 4 5 6 7 8 9 10

ENJOY TODAY

TODAY IS A GOOD DAY TO:

DATE: ______ / ______ / ______

MON TUE WED THU FRI SAT SUN

TODAY I AM FEELING:

THE WEATHER TODAY WAS:

TODAY I AM GRATEFUL FOR:

TO-DO LIST

MY FAVORITE PART OF TODAY WAS:

WHAT I ATE TODAY:

BREAKFAST	LUNCH	DINNER

NOTES:

DON'T FORGET!

DAILY INSPIRATION:

"The result justifies the deed."

-OVID

PRODUCTIVITY SCORE FOR TODAY:

1 2 3 4 5 6 7 8 9 10

ENJOY TODAY

TODAY IS A GOOD DAY TO:

DATE: ____ / ____ / ____

MON TUE WED THU FRI SAT SUN

TODAY I AM FEELING:

THE WEATHER TODAY WAS:

TODAY I AM GRATEFUL FOR:

TO-DO LIST

MY FAVORITE PART OF TODAY WAS:

WHAT I ATE TODAY:

BREAKFAST	LUNCH	DINNER

NOTES:

DON'T FORGET!

DAILY INSPIRATION:

"Creations of the mind are more alive than matter."

-CHARLES BAUDELAIRE

PRODUCTIVITY SCORE FOR TODAY:

1 2 3 4 5 6 7 8 9 10

Enjoy Today

TODAY IS A GOOD DAY TO:

DATE: ______ / ______ / ______

MON TUE WED THU FRI SAT SUN

TODAY I AM FEELING:

THE WEATHER TODAY WAS:

TODAY I AM GRATEFUL FOR:

TO-DO LIST

MY FAVORITE PART OF TODAY WAS:

WHAT I ATE TODAY:

BREAKFAST	LUNCH	DINNER

NOTES:

DON'T FORGET!

DAILY INSPIRATION:

"The use of criticism, in periodical writing, is to sift, not to stamp a work."

-MARGARET FULLER

PRODUCTIVITY SCORE FOR TODAY:

1 2 3 4 5 6 7 8 9 10

ENJOY TODAY

TODAY IS A GOOD DAY TO:

DATE: ____ / ____ / ____

MON TUE WED THU FRI SAT SUN

TODAY I AM FEELING:

THE WEATHER TODAY WAS:

TODAY I AM GRATEFUL FOR:

TO-DO LIST

MY FAVORITE PART OF TODAY WAS:

WHAT I ATE TODAY:

BREAKFAST	LUNCH	DINNER

NOTES:

DON'T FORGET!

DAILY INSPIRATION:

"Give thyself time to learn something new and good, and cease to be whirled around."

-MARCUS AURELIUS

PRODUCTIVITY SCORE FOR TODAY:

1 2 3 4 5 6 7 8 9 10

Enjoy Today

TODAY IS A GOOD DAY TO:

DATE: ____ / ____ / ____

MON TUE WED THU FRI SAT SUN

TODAY I AM FEELING:

THE WEATHER TODAY WAS:

TODAY I AM GRATEFUL FOR:

TO-DO LIST

MY FAVORITE PART OF TODAY WAS:

WHAT I ATE TODAY:

BREAKFAST	LUNCH	DINNER

NOTES:

DON'T FORGET!

DAILY INSPIRATION:

"Reason is not measured by size or height, but by principle."

-EPICTETUS

PRODUCTIVITY SCORE FOR TODAY:

1 2 3 4 5 6 7 8 9 10

ENJOY TODAY

TODAY IS A GOOD DAY TO:

DATE: ____ / ____ / ____

MON TUE WED THU FRI SAT SUN

TODAY I AM FEELING:

THE WEATHER TODAY WAS:

TODAY I AM GRATEFUL FOR:

TO-DO LIST

MY FAVORITE PART OF TODAY WAS:

WHAT I ATE TODAY:

BREAKFAST	LUNCH	DINNER

NOTES:

DON'T FORGET!

DAILY INSPIRATION:

"Adversity raises characters it does not degrade."

-LOUIS-PHILIPPE DE SÉGUR

PRODUCTIVITY SCORE FOR TODAY:

1 2 3 4 5 6 7 8 9 10

Enjoy Today

TODAY IS A GOOD DAY TO:

DATE: ____/____/____

MON TUE WED THU FRI SAT SUN

TODAY I AM FEELING:

THE WEATHER TODAY WAS:

TODAY I AM GRATEFUL FOR:

TO-DO LIST

MY FAVORITE PART OF TODAY WAS:

WHAT I ATE TODAY:

BREAKFAST	LUNCH	DINNER

NOTES:

DON'T FORGET!

DAILY INSPIRATION:

"Satire is a sort of glass, wherein beholders do generally discover everybody's face but their own."

-JONATHAN SWIFT

PRODUCTIVITY SCORE FOR TODAY:

1 2 3 4 5 6 7 8 9 10

Enjoy Today

TODAY IS A GOOD DAY TO:

DATE: ____ / ____ / ____

MON TUE WED THU FRI SAT SUN

TODAY I AM FEELING:

THE WEATHER TODAY WAS:

TODAY I AM GRATEFUL FOR:

TO-DO LIST

MY FAVORITE PART OF TODAY WAS:

WHAT I ATE TODAY:

BREAKFAST	LUNCH	DINNER

NOTES:

DON'T FORGET!

DAILY INSPIRATION:

"Many of life's failures are people who did not realize how close they were to success when they gave up."

-THOMAS EDISON

PRODUCTIVITY SCORE FOR TODAY:

1 2 3 4 5 6 7 8 9 10

ENJOY TODAY

TODAY IS A GOOD DAY TO:

DATE: ______ / ______ / ______

MON TUE WED THU FRI SAT SUN

TODAY I AM FEELING:

THE WEATHER TODAY WAS:

TODAY I AM GRATEFUL FOR:

TO-DO LIST

MY FAVORITE PART OF TODAY WAS:

WHAT I ATE TODAY:

BREAKFAST	LUNCH	DINNER

NOTES:

DON'T FORGET!

DAILY INSPIRATION:

"There is no time like the pleasant."

-OLIVER HERFORD

PRODUCTIVITY SCORE FOR TODAY:

1 2 3 4 5 6 7 8 9 10

ENJOY TODAY

TODAY IS A GOOD DAY TO:

DATE: ____ / ____ / ____

MON TUE WED THU FRI SAT SUN

TODAY I AM FEELING:

THE WEATHER TODAY WAS:

TODAY I AM GRATEFUL FOR:

TO-DO LIST

MY FAVORITE PART OF TODAY WAS:

WHAT I ATE TODAY:

BREAKFAST	LUNCH	DINNER

NOTES:

DON'T FORGET!

DAILY INSPIRATION:

"Life resembles a novel more often than novels resemble life."

-AMANDINE-AURORE-LUCILE DUPIN

PRODUCTIVITY SCORE FOR TODAY:

1 2 3 4 5 6 7 8 9 10

ENJOY TODAY

TODAY IS A GOOD DAY TO:

DATE: ____ / ____ / ____

MON TUE WED THU FRI SAT SUN

TODAY I AM FEELING:

THE WEATHER TODAY WAS:

TODAY I AM GRATEFUL FOR:

TO-DO LIST

MY FAVORITE PART OF TODAY WAS:

WHAT I ATE TODAY:

BREAKFAST	LUNCH	DINNER

NOTES:

DON'T FORGET!

DAILY INSPIRATION:

"All you need in this life is ignorance and confidence, and then Success is sure."

-MARK TWAIN

PRODUCTIVITY SCORE FOR TODAY:

1 2 3 4 5 6 7 8 9 10

ENJOY TODAY

TODAY IS A GOOD DAY TO:

DATE: ______ / ______ / ______

MON TUE WED THU FRI SAT SUN

TODAY I AM FEELING:

THE WEATHER TODAY WAS:

TODAY I AM GRATEFUL FOR:

TO-DO LIST

MY FAVORITE PART OF TODAY WAS:

WHAT I ATE TODAY:

BREAKFAST	LUNCH	DINNER

NOTES:

DON'T FORGET!

DAILY INSPIRATION:

"Forget the years, forget distinctions. Leap into the boundless and make it your home!"

-ZHUANGZI

PRODUCTIVITY SCORE FOR TODAY:

1 2 3 4 5 6 7 8 9 10

Enjoy Today

TODAY IS A GOOD DAY TO:

DATE: ______ / ______ / ______

MON TUE WED THU FRI SAT SUN

TODAY I AM FEELING:

THE WEATHER TODAY WAS:

TODAY I AM GRATEFUL FOR:

TO-DO LIST

MY FAVORITE PART OF TODAY WAS:

WHAT I ATE TODAY:

BREAKFAST	LUNCH	DINNER

NOTES:

DON'T FORGET!

DAILY INSPIRATION:

"There are no facts, only interpretations."

-FRIEDRICH NIETZSCHE

PRODUCTIVITY SCORE FOR TODAY:

1 2 3 4 5 6 7 8 9 10

ENJOY TODAY

TODAY IS A GOOD DAY TO:

DATE: ______ / ______ / ______

MON TUE WED THU FRI SAT SUN

TODAY I AM FEELING:

THE WEATHER TODAY WAS:

TODAY I AM GRATEFUL FOR:

TO-DO LIST

MY FAVORITE PART OF TODAY WAS:

WHAT I ATE TODAY:

BREAKFAST	LUNCH	DINNER

NOTES:

DON'T FORGET!

DAILY INSPIRATION:

"One never goes so far as when one doesn't know where one is going."

-JOHANN WOLFGANG VON GOETHE

PRODUCTIVITY SCORE FOR TODAY:

1 2 3 4 5 6 7 8 9 10

Enjoy Today

TODAY IS A GOOD DAY TO:

DATE: ____ / ____ / ____

MON TUE WED THU FRI SAT SUN

TODAY I AM FEELING:

THE WEATHER TODAY WAS:

TODAY I AM GRATEFUL FOR:

TO-DO LIST

MY FAVORITE PART OF TODAY WAS:

WHAT I ATE TODAY:

BREAKFAST	LUNCH	DINNER

NOTES:

DON'T FORGET!

DAILY INSPIRATION:

"A bone to the dog is not charity. Charity is the bone shared with the dog when you are just as hungry as the dog."

-JACK LONDON

PRODUCTIVITY SCORE FOR TODAY:

ENJOY TODAY

TODAY IS A GOOD DAY TO:

DATE: ____ / ____ / ____

MON TUE WED THU FRI SAT SUN

TODAY I AM FEELING:

THE WEATHER TODAY WAS:

TODAY I AM GRATEFUL FOR:

TO-DO LIST

MY FAVORITE PART OF TODAY WAS:

WHAT I ATE TODAY:

BREAKFAST	LUNCH	DINNER

NOTES:

DON'T FORGET!

DAILY INSPIRATION:

"Dishonesty will stare honesty out of countenance, any day in the week, if there is anything to be got by it."

-CHARLES DICKENS

PRODUCTIVITY SCORE FOR TODAY:

1 2 3 4 5 6 7 8 9 10

ENJOY TODAY

TODAY IS A GOOD DAY TO:

DATE: ______ / ______ / ______

MON TUE WED THU FRI SAT SUN

TODAY I AM FEELING:

THE WEATHER TODAY WAS:

TODAY I AM GRATEFUL FOR:

TO-DO LIST

MY FAVORITE PART OF TODAY WAS:

WHAT I ATE TODAY:

BREAKFAST	LUNCH	DINNER

NOTES:

DON'T FORGET!

DAILY INSPIRATION:

"He who fears being conquered is certain of defeat."

-NAPOLÉON BONAPARTE

PRODUCTIVITY SCORE FOR TODAY:

1 2 3 4 5 6 7 8 9 10

ENJOY TODAY

TODAY IS A GOOD DAY TO:

DATE: ______ / ______ / ______

MON TUE WED THU FRI SAT SUN

TODAY I AM FEELING:

THE WEATHER TODAY WAS:

TODAY I AM GRATEFUL FOR:

TO-DO LIST

MY FAVORITE PART OF TODAY WAS:

WHAT I ATE TODAY:

BREAKFAST	LUNCH	DINNER

NOTES:

DON'T FORGET!

DAILY INSPIRATION:

"Knowledge is folly unless grace guide it."

-GEORGE HERBERT

PRODUCTIVITY SCORE FOR TODAY:

1 2 3 4 5 6 7 8 9 10

ENJOY TODAY

TODAY IS A GOOD DAY TO:

DATE: ______ / ______ / ______

MON TUE WED THU FRI SAT SUN

TODAY I AM FEELING:

THE WEATHER TODAY WAS:

TODAY I AM GRATEFUL FOR:

TO-DO LIST

MY FAVORITE PART OF TODAY WAS:

WHAT I ATE TODAY:

BREAKFAST	LUNCH	DINNER

NOTES:

DON'T FORGET!

DAILY INSPIRATION:

"Knowledge may give weight, but accomplishments give lustre, and many more people see than weigh."

-COUNT OF CHESTERFIELD

PRODUCTIVITY SCORE FOR TODAY:

1 2 3 4 5 6 7 8 9 10

ENJOY TODAY

TODAY IS A GOOD DAY TO:

DATE: _____ / _____ / _____

MON TUE WED THU FRI SAT SUN

TODAY I AM FEELING:

THE WEATHER TODAY WAS:

TODAY I AM GRATEFUL FOR:

TO-DO LIST

MY FAVORITE PART OF TODAY WAS:

WHAT I ATE TODAY:

BREAKFAST	LUNCH	DINNER

NOTES:

DON'T FORGET!

DAILY INSPIRATION:

"Meanings are not determined by situations, but we determine ourselves by the meanings we give to situations."

-ALFRED ADLER

PRODUCTIVITY SCORE FOR TODAY:

1 2 3 4 5 6 7 8 9 10

ENJOY TODAY

TODAY IS A GOOD DAY TO:

DATE: ____ / ____ / ____

MON TUE WED THU FRI SAT SUN

TODAY I AM FEELING:

THE WEATHER TODAY WAS:

TODAY I AM GRATEFUL FOR:

TO-DO LIST

MY FAVORITE PART OF TODAY WAS:

WHAT I ATE TODAY:

BREAKFAST	LUNCH	DINNER

NOTES:

DON'T FORGET!

DAILY INSPIRATION:

"The direction of the mind is more important than its progress."

-JOSEPH JOUBERT

PRODUCTIVITY SCORE FOR TODAY:

1 2 3 4 5 6 7 8 9 10

ENJOY TODAY

TODAY IS A GOOD DAY TO:

DATE: ____ / ____ / ____

MON TUE WED THU FRI SAT SUN

TODAY I AM FEELING:

THE WEATHER TODAY WAS:

TODAY I AM GRATEFUL FOR:

TO-DO LIST

MY FAVORITE PART OF TODAY WAS:

WHAT I ATE TODAY:

BREAKFAST	LUNCH	DINNER

NOTES:

DON'T FORGET!

DAILY INSPIRATION:

"The dictates of the heart are the voice of fate."

-JOHANN CHRISTOPH FRIEDRICH VON SCHILLER

PRODUCTIVITY SCORE FOR TODAY:

1 2 3 4 5 6 7 8 9 10

ENJOY TODAY

TODAY IS A GOOD DAY TO:

DATE: ____/____/____

MON TUE WED THU FRI SAT SUN

TODAY I AM FEELING:

THE WEATHER TODAY WAS:

TODAY I AM GRATEFUL FOR:

TO-DO LIST

MY FAVORITE PART OF TODAY WAS:

WHAT I ATE TODAY:

BREAKFAST	LUNCH	DINNER

NOTES:

DON'T FORGET!

DAILY INSPIRATION:

"Blessed is he who expects nothing, for he shall never be disappointed."

-ALEXANDER POPE

PRODUCTIVITY SCORE FOR TODAY:

1 2 3 4 5 6 7 8 9 10

ENJOY TODAY

TODAY IS A GOOD DAY TO:

DATE: ____ / ____ / ____

MON TUE WED THU FRI SAT SUN

TODAY I AM FEELING:

THE WEATHER TODAY WAS:

TODAY I AM GRATEFUL FOR:

TO-DO LIST

MY FAVORITE PART OF TODAY WAS:

WHAT I ATE TODAY:

BREAKFAST	LUNCH	DINNER

NOTES:

DON'T FORGET!

DAILY INSPIRATION:

"One half of the world cannot understand the pleasures of the other."

-JANE AUSTEN

PRODUCTIVITY SCORE FOR TODAY:

1 2 3 4 5 6 7 8 9 10

Enjoy Today

TODAY IS A GOOD DAY TO:

DATE: ____ / ____ / ____

MON TUE WED THU FRI SAT SUN

TODAY I AM FEELING:

THE WEATHER TODAY WAS:

TODAY I AM GRATEFUL FOR:

TO-DO LIST

MY FAVORITE PART OF TODAY WAS:

WHAT I ATE TODAY:

BREAKFAST	LUNCH	DINNER

NOTES:

DON'T FORGET!

DAILY INSPIRATION:

"Poor is the pupil that does not surpass his master."

-LEONARDO DA VINCI

PRODUCTIVITY SCORE FOR TODAY:

1 2 3 4 5 6 7 8 9 10

ENJOY TODAY

TODAY IS A GOOD DAY TO:

DATE: ____ / ____ / ____

MON TUE WED THU FRI SAT SUN

TODAY I AM FEELING:

THE WEATHER TODAY WAS:

TODAY I AM GRATEFUL FOR:

TO-DO LIST

MY FAVORITE PART OF TODAY WAS:

WHAT I ATE TODAY:

BREAKFAST	LUNCH	DINNER

NOTES:

DON'T FORGET!

DAILY INSPIRATION:

"The imitator dooms himself to hopeless mediocrity."

-RALPH WALDO EMERSON

PRODUCTIVITY SCORE FOR TODAY:

1 2 3 4 5 6 7 8 9 10

ENJOY TODAY

TODAY IS A GOOD DAY TO:

DATE: ____ / ____ / ____

MON TUE WED THU FRI SAT SUN

TODAY I AM FEELING:

THE WEATHER TODAY WAS:

TODAY I AM GRATEFUL FOR:

TO-DO LIST

MY FAVORITE PART OF TODAY WAS:

WHAT I ATE TODAY:

BREAKFAST	LUNCH	DINNER

NOTES:

DON'T FORGET!

DAILY INSPIRATION:

"To have a right to do a thing is not at all the same as to be right in doing it."

-GILBERT KEITH CHESTERTON

PRODUCTIVITY SCORE FOR TODAY:

1 2 3 4 5 6 7 8 9 10

Enjoy Today

TODAY IS A GOOD DAY TO:

DATE: ______ / ______ / ______

MON TUE WED THU FRI SAT SUN

TODAY I AM FEELING:

THE WEATHER TODAY WAS:

TODAY I AM GRATEFUL FOR:

TO-DO LIST

MY FAVORITE PART OF TODAY WAS:

WHAT I ATE TODAY:

BREAKFAST	LUNCH	DINNER

NOTES:

DON'T FORGET!

DAILY INSPIRATION:

"Talent hits a target no one else can hit; Genius hits a target no one else can see."

-ARTHUR SCHOPENHAUER

PRODUCTIVITY SCORE FOR TODAY:

1 2 3 4 5 6 7 8 9 10

Enjoy Today

TODAY IS A GOOD DAY TO:

DATE: ______ / ______ / ______

MON TUE WED THU FRI SAT SUN

TODAY I AM FEELING:

THE WEATHER TODAY WAS:

TODAY I AM GRATEFUL FOR:

TO-DO LIST

MY FAVORITE PART OF TODAY WAS:

WHAT I ATE TODAY:

BREAKFAST	LUNCH	DINNER

NOTES:

DON'T FORGET!

DAILY INSPIRATION:

"Happiness is a good flow of life."

-ZENO OF CITIUM

PRODUCTIVITY SCORE FOR TODAY:

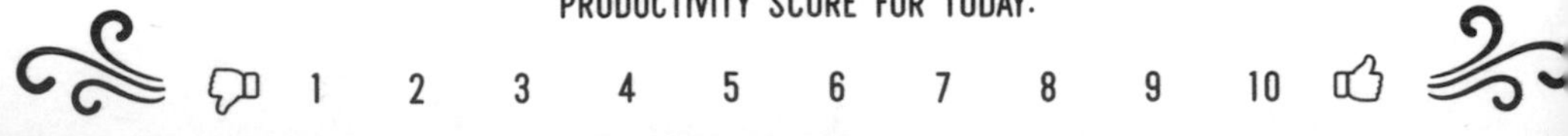

ENJOY TODAY

TODAY IS A GOOD DAY TO:

DATE: ____ / ____ / ____

MON TUE WED THU FRI SAT SUN

TODAY I AM FEELING:

THE WEATHER TODAY WAS:

TODAY I AM GRATEFUL FOR:

TO-DO LIST

MY FAVORITE PART OF TODAY WAS:

WHAT I ATE TODAY:

BREAKFAST	LUNCH	DINNER

NOTES:

DON'T FORGET!

DAILY INSPIRATION:

"Desperation is sometimes as powerful an inspirer as genius."

-BENJAMIN DISRAELI

PRODUCTIVITY SCORE FOR TODAY:

1 2 3 4 5 6 7 8 9 10

Enjoy Today

TODAY IS A GOOD DAY TO:

DATE: ____ / ____ / ____

MON TUE WED THU FRI SAT SUN

TODAY I AM FEELING:

THE WEATHER TODAY WAS:

TODAY I AM GRATEFUL FOR:

TO-DO LIST

MY FAVORITE PART OF TODAY WAS:

WHAT I ATE TODAY:

BREAKFAST	LUNCH	DINNER

NOTES:

DON'T FORGET!

DAILY INSPIRATION:

"Go confidently in the direction of your dreams! Live the life you've imagined."

-HENRY DAVID THOREAU

PRODUCTIVITY SCORE FOR TODAY:

1 2 3 4 5 6 7 8 9 10

TODAY IS A GOOD DAY TO:

DATE: ____/____/____

ENJOY TODAY

MON TUE WED THU FRI SAT SUN

TODAY I AM FEELING:

THE WEATHER TODAY WAS:

TODAY I AM GRATEFUL FOR:

TO-DO LIST

MY FAVORITE PART OF TODAY WAS:

WHAT I ATE TODAY:

BREAKFAST	LUNCH	DINNER

NOTES:

DON'T FORGET!

DAILY INSPIRATION:

"None has begun to think how divine he himself is and how certain the future is."

-WALT WHITMAN

PRODUCTIVITY SCORE FOR TODAY:

1 2 3 4 5 6 7 8 9 10

Enjoy Today

TODAY IS A GOOD DAY TO:

DATE: ____ / ____ / ____

MON TUE WED THU FRI SAT SUN

TODAY I AM FEELING:

THE WEATHER TODAY WAS:

TODAY I AM GRATEFUL FOR:

TO-DO LIST

MY FAVORITE PART OF TODAY WAS:

WHAT I ATE TODAY:

BREAKFAST	LUNCH	DINNER

NOTES:

DON'T FORGET!

DAILY INSPIRATION:

"Culture is the victory of boredom over self-esteem."

-ÉMILE FAGUET

PRODUCTIVITY SCORE FOR TODAY:

ENJOY TODAY

TODAY IS A GOOD DAY TO:

DATE: ____ /____ /____

MON TUE WED THU FRI SAT SUN

TODAY I AM FEELING:

THE WEATHER TODAY WAS:

TODAY I AM GRATEFUL FOR:

TO-DO LIST

MY FAVORITE PART OF TODAY WAS:

WHAT I ATE TODAY:

BREAKFAST	LUNCH	DINNER

NOTES:

DON'T FORGET!

DAILY INSPIRATION:

"We turn not older with years, but newer every day."

-EMILY DICKINSON

PRODUCTIVITY SCORE FOR TODAY:

1 2 3 4 5 6 7 8 9 10

TODAY IS A GOOD DAY TO:

DATE: ____ / ____ / ____

MON TUE WED THU FRI SAT SUN

TODAY I AM FEELING:

THE WEATHER TODAY WAS:

TODAY I AM GRATEFUL FOR:

TO-DO LIST

MY FAVORITE PART OF TODAY WAS:

WHAT I ATE TODAY:

BREAKFAST	LUNCH	DINNER

NOTES:

DON'T FORGET!

DAILY INSPIRATION:

"A man who dares to waste one hour of time has not discovered the value of life."

-CHARLES DARWIN

PRODUCTIVITY SCORE FOR TODAY:

1 2 3 4 5 6 7 8 9 10

ENJOY TODAY

TODAY IS A GOOD DAY TO:

DATE: ____/____/____

MON TUE WED THU FRI SAT SUN

TODAY I AM FEELING:

THE WEATHER TODAY WAS:

TODAY I AM GRATEFUL FOR:

TO-DO LIST

MY FAVORITE PART OF TODAY WAS:

WHAT I ATE TODAY:

BREAKFAST	LUNCH	DINNER

NOTES:

DON'T FORGET!

DAILY INSPIRATION:

"Truth is ever incoherent, and when the big hearts strike together, the concussion is a little stunning."

-HERMAN MELVILLE

PRODUCTIVITY SCORE FOR TODAY:

1 2 3 4 5 6 7 8 9 10

ENJOY TODAY

TODAY IS A GOOD DAY TO:

DATE: ____/____/____

MON TUE WED THU FRI SAT SUN

TODAY I AM FEELING:

THE WEATHER TODAY WAS:

TODAY I AM GRATEFUL FOR:

TO-DO LIST

MY FAVORITE PART OF TODAY WAS:

WHAT I ATE TODAY:

BREAKFAST	LUNCH	DINNER

NOTES:

DON'T FORGET!

DAILY INSPIRATION:

"Keep your eyes on the stars, but remember to keep your feet on the ground."

-THEODORE ROOSEVELT

PRODUCTIVITY SCORE FOR TODAY:

1 2 3 4 5 6 7 8 9 10

ENJOY TODAY

TODAY IS A GOOD DAY TO:

DATE: ____ /____ /____

MON TUE WED THU FRI SAT SUN

TODAY I AM FEELING:

THE WEATHER TODAY WAS:

TODAY I AM GRATEFUL FOR:

TO-DO LIST

MY FAVORITE PART OF TODAY WAS:

WHAT I ATE TODAY:

BREAKFAST	LUNCH	DINNER

NOTES:

DON'T FORGET!

DAILY INSPIRATION:

"A friend is someone who knows all about you and still loves you."

-ELBERT HUBBARD

PRODUCTIVITY SCORE FOR TODAY:

1 2 3 4 5 6 7 8 9 10

Enjoy Today

TODAY IS A GOOD DAY TO:

DATE: ____ / ____ / ____

MON TUE WED THU FRI SAT SUN

TODAY I AM FEELING:

THE WEATHER TODAY WAS:

TODAY I AM GRATEFUL FOR:

TO-DO LIST

MY FAVORITE PART OF TODAY WAS:

WHAT I ATE TODAY:

BREAKFAST	LUNCH	DINNER

NOTES:

DON'T FORGET!

DAILY INSPIRATION:

"If there is but little water in the stream, it is the fault, not of the channel, but of the source."

-SAINT JEROME

PRODUCTIVITY SCORE FOR TODAY:

1 2 3 4 5 6 7 8 9 10

ENJOY TODAY

TODAY IS A GOOD DAY TO:

DATE: ____ / ____ / ____

MON TUE WED THU FRI SAT SUN

TODAY I AM FEELING:

THE WEATHER TODAY WAS:

TODAY I AM GRATEFUL FOR:

TO-DO LIST

MY FAVORITE PART OF TODAY WAS:

WHAT I ATE TODAY:

BREAKFAST	LUNCH	DINNER

NOTES:

DON'T FORGET!

DAILY INSPIRATION:

"There is nothing that makes its way more directly to the soul than beauty."

-JOSEPH ADDISON

PRODUCTIVITY SCORE FOR TODAY:

1 2 3 4 5 6 7 8 9 10

ENJOY TODAY

TODAY IS A GOOD DAY TO:

DATE: ____ / ____ / ____

MON TUE WED THU FRI SAT SUN

TODAY I AM FEELING:

THE WEATHER TODAY WAS:

TODAY I AM GRATEFUL FOR:

TO-DO LIST

MY FAVORITE PART OF TODAY WAS:

WHAT I ATE TODAY:

BREAKFAST	LUNCH	DINNER

NOTES:

DON'T FORGET!

DAILY INSPIRATION:

"All the opinions in the world point out that pleasure is our aim."

-MICHEL DE MONTAIGNE

PRODUCTIVITY SCORE FOR TODAY:

1 2 3 4 5 6 7 8 9 10

ENJOY TODAY

TODAY IS A GOOD DAY TO:

DATE: ____/____/____

MON TUE WED THU FRI SAT SUN

TODAY I AM FEELING:

THE WEATHER TODAY WAS:

TODAY I AM GRATEFUL FOR:

TO-DO LIST

MY FAVORITE PART OF TODAY WAS:

WHAT I ATE TODAY:

BREAKFAST	LUNCH	DINNER

NOTES:

DON'T FORGET!

DAILY INSPIRATION:

"The dreamers are the saviours of the world."

-JAMES ALLEN

PRODUCTIVITY SCORE FOR TODAY:

1 2 3 4 5 6 7 8 9 10

ENJOY TODAY

TODAY IS A GOOD DAY TO:

DATE: ____ / ____ / ____

MON TUE WED THU FRI SAT SUN

TODAY I AM FEELING:

THE WEATHER TODAY WAS:

TODAY I AM GRATEFUL FOR:

TO-DO LIST

MY FAVORITE PART OF TODAY WAS:

WHAT I ATE TODAY:

BREAKFAST	LUNCH	DINNER

NOTES:

DON'T FORGET!

DAILY INSPIRATION:

"Peace is more important than all justice; and peace was not made for the sake of justice, but justice for the sake of peace."

-MARTIN LUTHER

PRODUCTIVITY SCORE FOR TODAY:

1 2 3 4 5 6 7 8 9 10

ENJOY TODAY

TODAY IS A GOOD DAY TO:

DATE: ____ / ____ / ____

MON TUE WED THU FRI SAT SUN

TODAY I AM FEELING:

THE WEATHER TODAY WAS:

TODAY I AM GRATEFUL FOR:

TO-DO LIST

MY FAVORITE PART OF TODAY WAS:

WHAT I ATE TODAY:

BREAKFAST	LUNCH	DINNER

NOTES:

DON'T FORGET!

DAILY INSPIRATION:

"Every plan should be adopted,
every experiment tried,
which may do something towards
the ultimate object."

-THOMAS JEFFERSON

PRODUCTIVITY SCORE FOR TODAY:

1 2 3 4 5 6 7 8 9 10

Enjoy Today

TODAY IS A GOOD DAY TO:

DATE: ____/____/____

MON TUE WED THU FRI SAT SUN

TODAY I AM FEELING:

THE WEATHER TODAY WAS:

TODAY I AM GRATEFUL FOR:

TO-DO LIST

MY FAVORITE PART OF TODAY WAS:

WHAT I ATE TODAY:

BREAKFAST	LUNCH	DINNER

NOTES:

DON'T FORGET!

DAILY INSPIRATION:

"If you tell the truth you don't have to remember anything."

-MARK TWAIN

PRODUCTIVITY SCORE FOR TODAY:

1 2 3 4 5 6 7 8 9 10

ENJOY TODAY

ODAY IS A GOOD DAY TO:

DATE: _____ / _____ / _____

MON TUE WED THU FRI SAT SUN

ODAY I AM FEELING:

THE WEATHER TODAY WAS:

ODAY I AM GRATEFUL FOR:

TO-DO LIST

Y FAVORITE PART OF TODAY WAS:

HAT I ATE TODAY:

BREAKFAST	LUNCH	DINNER

OTES:

DON'T FORGET!

DAILY INSPIRATION:

"Life grants nothing to us mortals without hard work."

-HORACE

PRODUCTIVITY SCORE FOR TODAY:

1 2 3 4 5 6 7 8 9 10

ENJOY TODAY

TODAY IS A GOOD DAY TO:

DATE: ____ / ____ / ____

MON TUE WED THU FRI SAT SUN

TODAY I AM FEELING:

THE WEATHER TODAY WAS:

TODAY I AM GRATEFUL FOR:

TO-DO LIST

MY FAVORITE PART OF TODAY WAS:

WHAT I ATE TODAY:

BREAKFAST	LUNCH	DINNER

NOTES:

DON'T FORGET!

DAILY INSPIRATION:

"The fault, dear Brutus, is not in our stars, But in ourselves, that we are underlings."

-WILLIAM SHAKESPEARE

PRODUCTIVITY SCORE FOR TODAY:

1 2 3 4 5 6 7 8 9 10

ENJOY TODAY

TODAY IS A GOOD DAY TO:

DATE: ____ / ____ / ____

MON TUE WED THU FRI SAT SUN

TODAY I AM FEELING:

THE WEATHER TODAY WAS:

TODAY I AM GRATEFUL FOR:

TO-DO LIST

MY FAVORITE PART OF TODAY WAS:

WHAT I ATE TODAY:

BREAKFAST	LUNCH	DINNER

NOTES:

DON'T FORGET!

DAILY INSPIRATION:

"We never understand how little we need in this world until we know the loss of it."

-JAMES M. BARRIE

PRODUCTIVITY SCORE FOR TODAY:

1 2 3 4 5 6 7 8 9 10

ENJOY TODAY

TODAY IS A GOOD DAY TO:

DATE: ______ / ______ / ______

MON TUE WED THU FRI SAT SUN

TODAY I AM FEELING:

THE WEATHER TODAY WAS:

TODAY I AM GRATEFUL FOR:

TO-DO LIST

MY FAVORITE PART OF TODAY WAS:

WHAT I ATE TODAY:

BREAKFAST	LUNCH	DINNER

NOTES:

DON'T FORGET!

DAILY INSPIRATION:

"To be well-informed is to have the world at your fingers."

-JOSEPH JONES

PRODUCTIVITY SCORE FOR TODAY:

1 2 3 4 5 6 7 8 9 10

ENJOY TODAY

TODAY IS A GOOD DAY TO:

DATE: ____ / ____ / ____

MON TUE WED THU FRI SAT SUN

TODAY I AM FEELING:

THE WEATHER TODAY WAS:

TODAY I AM GRATEFUL FOR:

TO-DO LIST

MY FAVORITE PART OF TODAY WAS:

WHAT I ATE TODAY:

BREAKFAST	LUNCH	DINNER

NOTES:

DON'T FORGET!

DAILY INSPIRATION:

"Stand fast among the beamlike spears."

-ARCHILOCHUS

PRODUCTIVITY SCORE FOR TODAY:

1 2 3 4 5 6 7 8 9 10

ENJOY TODAY

TODAY IS A GOOD DAY TO:

DATE: ______ / ______ / ______

MON TUE WED THU FRI SAT SUN

TODAY I AM FEELING:

THE WEATHER TODAY WAS:

TODAY I AM GRATEFUL FOR:

TO-DO LIST

MY FAVORITE PART OF TODAY WAS:

WHAT I ATE TODAY:

BREAKFAST	LUNCH	DINNER

NOTES:

DON'T FORGET!

DAILY INSPIRATION:

"Freedom's possibility is not the ability to choose the good or the evil. The possibility is to be able."

–SØREN KIERKEGAARD

PRODUCTIVITY SCORE FOR TODAY:

1 2 3 4 5 6 7 8 9 10

ENJOY TODAY

TODAY IS A GOOD DAY TO:

DATE: ____/____/____

MON TUE WED THU FRI SAT SUN

TODAY I AM FEELING:

THE WEATHER TODAY WAS:

TODAY I AM GRATEFUL FOR:

TO-DO LIST

MY FAVORITE PART OF TODAY WAS:

WHAT I ATE TODAY:

BREAKFAST	LUNCH	DINNER

NOTES:

DON'T FORGET!

DAILY INSPIRATION:

"Nothing is so fatiguing as the eternal hanging on of an uncompleted task."

-WILLIAM JAMES

PRODUCTIVITY SCORE FOR TODAY:

1 2 3 4 5 6 7 8 9 10

ENJOY TODAY

TODAY IS A GOOD DAY TO:

DATE: ____ / ____ / ____

MON TUE WED THU FRI SAT SUN

TODAY I AM FEELING:

THE WEATHER TODAY WAS:

TODAY I AM GRATEFUL FOR:

TO-DO LIST

MY FAVORITE PART OF TODAY WAS:

WHAT I ATE TODAY:

BREAKFAST	LUNCH	DINNER

NOTES:

DON'T FORGET!

DAILY INSPIRATION:

"The true method of knowledge is experiment."

-WILLIAM BLAKE

PRODUCTIVITY SCORE FOR TODAY:

1 2 3 4 5 6 7 8 9 10

ENJOY TODAY

TODAY IS A GOOD DAY TO:

DATE: ____/____/____

MON TUE WED THU FRI SAT SUN

TODAY I AM FEELING:

THE WEATHER TODAY WAS:

TODAY I AM GRATEFUL FOR:

TO-DO LIST

MY FAVORITE PART OF TODAY WAS:

WHAT I ATE TODAY:

BREAKFAST	LUNCH	DINNER

NOTES:

DON'T FORGET!

DAILY INSPIRATION:

"Love is space and time made tender to the heart."

-MARCEL PROUST

PRODUCTIVITY SCORE FOR TODAY:

1 2 3 4 5 6 7 8 9 10

ENJOY TODAY

TODAY IS A GOOD DAY TO:

DATE: ____/____/____

MON TUE WED THU FRI SAT SUN

TODAY I AM FEELING:

THE WEATHER TODAY WAS:

TODAY I AM GRATEFUL FOR:

TO-DO LIST

MY FAVORITE PART OF TODAY WAS:

WHAT I ATE TODAY:

BREAKFAST	LUNCH	DINNER

NOTES:

DON'T FORGET!

DAILY INSPIRATION:

"The true wisdom is to be always seasonable, and to change with a good grace in changing circumstances."

-ROBERT LOUIS STEVENSON

PRODUCTIVITY SCORE FOR TODAY:

1 2 3 4 5 6 7 8 9 10

ENJOY TODAY

TODAY IS A GOOD DAY TO:

DATE: ____ / ____ / ____

MON TUE WED THU FRI SAT SUN

TODAY I AM FEELING:

THE WEATHER TODAY WAS:

TODAY I AM GRATEFUL FOR:

TO-DO LIST

MY FAVORITE PART OF TODAY WAS:

WHAT I ATE TODAY:

BREAKFAST	LUNCH	DINNER

NOTES:

DON'T FORGET!

DAILY INSPIRATION:

"Beyond a certain point
there is no return.
This point has to be reached."

-FRANZ KAFKA

PRODUCTIVITY SCORE FOR TODAY:

1 2 3 4 5 6 7 8 9 10

Enjoy Today

TODAY IS A GOOD DAY TO:

DATE: ____/____/____

MON TUE WED THU FRI SAT SUN

TODAY I AM FEELING:

THE WEATHER TODAY WAS:

TODAY I AM GRATEFUL FOR:

TO-DO LIST

MY FAVORITE PART OF TODAY WAS:

WHAT I ATE TODAY:

BREAKFAST	LUNCH	DINNER

NOTES:

DON'T FORGET!

DAILY INSPIRATION:

"What you do not want done to yourself, do not do to others."

-CONFUCIUS

PRODUCTIVITY SCORE FOR TODAY:

1 2 3 4 5 6 7 8 9 10

ENJOY TODAY

TODAY IS A GOOD DAY TO:

DATE: ____ / ____ / ____

MON TUE WED THU FRI SAT SUN

TODAY I AM FEELING:

THE WEATHER TODAY WAS:

TODAY I AM GRATEFUL FOR:

TO-DO LIST

MY FAVORITE PART OF TODAY WAS:

WHAT I ATE TODAY:

BREAKFAST	LUNCH	DINNER

NOTES:

DON'T FORGET!

DAILY INSPIRATION:

"Our life is frittered away by detail. Simplify, simplify."

-HENRY DAVID THOREAU

PRODUCTIVITY SCORE FOR TODAY:

1 2 3 4 5 6 7 8 9 10

ENJOY TODAY

TODAY IS A GOOD DAY TO:

DATE: ______ / ______ / ______

MON TUE WED THU FRI SAT SUN

TODAY I AM FEELING:

THE WEATHER TODAY WAS:

TODAY I AM GRATEFUL FOR:

TO-DO LIST

MY FAVORITE PART OF TODAY WAS:

WHAT I ATE TODAY:

BREAKFAST	LUNCH	DINNER

NOTES:

DON'T FORGET!

DAILY INSPIRATION:

"Life is not always a matter of holding good cards, but sometimes, playing a poor hand well."

-JACK LONDON

PRODUCTIVITY SCORE FOR TODAY:

1 2 3 4 5 6 7 8 9 10

ENJOY TODAY

TODAY IS A GOOD DAY TO:

DATE: ____ / ____ / ____

MON TUE WED THU FRI SAT SUN

TODAY I AM FEELING:

THE WEATHER TODAY WAS:

TODAY I AM GRATEFUL FOR:

TO-DO LIST

MY FAVORITE PART OF TODAY WAS:

WHAT I ATE TODAY:

BREAKFAST	LUNCH	DINNER

NOTES:

DON'T FORGET!

DAILY INSPIRATION:

"There is neither happiness nor misery in the world; there is only the comparison of one state with another, nothing more."

-ALEXANDRE DUMAS

PRODUCTIVITY SCORE FOR TODAY:

1 2 3 4 5 6 7 8 9 10

Enjoy Today

TODAY IS A GOOD DAY TO:

DATE: ______ / ______ / ______

MON TUE WED THU FRI SAT SUN

TODAY I AM FEELING:

THE WEATHER TODAY WAS:

TODAY I AM GRATEFUL FOR:

TO-DO LIST

MY FAVORITE PART OF TODAY WAS:

WHAT I ATE TODAY:

BREAKFAST	LUNCH	DINNER

NOTES:

DON'T FORGET!

DAILY INSPIRATION:

"Compassion is the basis of all morality."

-ARTHUR SCHOPENHAUER

PRODUCTIVITY SCORE FOR TODAY:

1 2 3 4 5 6 7 8 9 10

Enjoy Today

TODAY IS A GOOD DAY TO:

DATE: ____ / ____ / ____

MON TUE WED THU FRI SAT SUN

TODAY I AM FEELING:

THE WEATHER TODAY WAS:

TODAY I AM GRATEFUL FOR:

TO-DO LIST

MY FAVORITE PART OF TODAY WAS:

WHAT I ATE TODAY:

BREAKFAST	LUNCH	DINNER

NOTES:

DON'T FORGET!

DAILY INSPIRATION:

"One must be something in order to do something."

-JOHANN WOLFGANG VON GOETHE

PRODUCTIVITY SCORE FOR TODAY:

1 2 3 4 5 6 7 8 9 10

ENJOY TODAY

TODAY IS A GOOD DAY TO:

DATE: ____ / ____ / ____

MON TUE WED THU FRI SAT SUN

TODAY I AM FEELING:

THE WEATHER TODAY WAS:

TODAY I AM GRATEFUL FOR:

TO-DO LIST

MY FAVORITE PART OF TODAY WAS:

WHAT I ATE TODAY:

BREAKFAST	LUNCH	DINNER

NOTES:

DON'T FORGET!

DAILY INSPIRATION:

"The reading of all good books is like conversation with the finest men of past centuries."

-RENÉ DESCARTES

PRODUCTIVITY SCORE FOR TODAY:

1 2 3 4 5 6 7 8 9 10

ENJOY TODAY

TODAY IS A GOOD DAY TO:

DATE: ____/____/____

MON TUE WED THU FRI SAT SUN

TODAY I AM FEELING:

THE WEATHER TODAY WAS:

TODAY I AM GRATEFUL FOR:

TO-DO LIST

MY FAVORITE PART OF TODAY WAS:

WHAT I ATE TODAY:

BREAKFAST	LUNCH	DINNER

NOTES:

DON'T FORGET!

DAILY INSPIRATION:

"Trust not too much to that enchanting face: Beauty's a charm, but soon the charm will pass."

-VIRGIL

PRODUCTIVITY SCORE FOR TODAY:

1 2 3 4 5 6 7 8 9 10

ENJOY TODAY

TODAY IS A GOOD DAY TO:

DATE: ____/____/____

MON TUE WED THU FRI SAT SU

TODAY I AM FEELING:

THE WEATHER TODAY WAS:

TODAY I AM GRATEFUL FOR:

TO-DO LIST

MY FAVORITE PART OF TODAY WAS:

WHAT I ATE TODAY:

BREAKFAST	LUNCH	DINNER

NOTES:

DON'T FORGET!

DAILY INSPIRATION:

"Man knows much more than he understands."

-ALFRED ADLER

PRODUCTIVITY SCORE FOR TODAY:

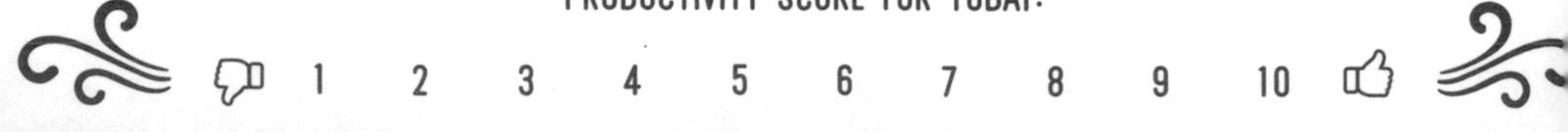

ENJOY TODAY

TODAY IS A GOOD DAY TO:

DATE: ______ / ______ / ______

MON TUE WED THU FRI SAT SUN

TODAY I AM FEELING:

THE WEATHER TODAY WAS:

TODAY I AM GRATEFUL FOR:

TO-DO LIST

MY FAVORITE PART OF TODAY WAS:

WHAT I ATE TODAY:

BREAKFAST	LUNCH	DINNER

NOTES:

DON'T FORGET!

DAILY INSPIRATION:

"To save all we must risk all."

–JOHANN CHRISTOPH FRIEDRICH VON SCHILLER

PRODUCTIVITY SCORE FOR TODAY:

1 2 3 4 5 6 7 8 9 10

Enjoy Today

TODAY IS A GOOD DAY TO:

DATE: ______ / ______ / ______

MON TUE WED THU FRI SAT SUN

TODAY I AM FEELING:

THE WEATHER TODAY WAS:

TODAY I AM GRATEFUL FOR:

TO-DO LIST

MY FAVORITE PART OF TODAY WAS:

WHAT I ATE TODAY:

BREAKFAST	LUNCH	DINNER

NOTES:

DON'T FORGET!

DAILY INSPIRATION:

"Knowledge of the fact differs from knowledge of the reason for the fact."

-ARISTOTLE

PRODUCTIVITY SCORE FOR TODAY:

1 2 3 4 5 6 7 8 9 10

Enjoy Today

TODAY IS A GOOD DAY TO:

DATE: ______ / ______ / ______

MON TUE WED THU FRI SAT SUN

TODAY I AM FEELING:

THE WEATHER TODAY WAS:

TODAY I AM GRATEFUL FOR:

TO-DO LIST

MY FAVORITE PART OF TODAY WAS:

WHAT I ATE TODAY:

BREAKFAST	LUNCH	DINNER

NOTES:

DON'T FORGET!

DAILY INSPIRATION:

"Modesty is the gentle art of enhancing your charm by pretending not to be aware of it."

-OLIVER HERFORD

PRODUCTIVITY SCORE FOR TODAY:

1 2 3 4 5 6 7 8 9 10

ENJOY TODAY

TODAY IS A GOOD DAY TO:

DATE: ______ / ______ / ______

MON TUE WED THU FRI SAT SUN

TODAY I AM FEELING:

THE WEATHER TODAY WAS:

TODAY I AM GRATEFUL FOR:

TO-DO LIST

MY FAVORITE PART OF TODAY WAS:

WHAT I ATE TODAY:

BREAKFAST	LUNCH	DINNER

NOTES:

DON'T FORGET!

DAILY INSPIRATION:

"To forget time, to forgive life, to be at peace."

-OSCAR WILDE

PRODUCTIVITY SCORE FOR TODAY:

1 2 3 4 5 6 7 8 9 10

ENJOY TODAY

TODAY IS A GOOD DAY TO:

DATE: ______ / ______ / ______

MON TUE WED THU FRI SAT SUN

TODAY I AM FEELING:

THE WEATHER TODAY WAS:

TODAY I AM GRATEFUL FOR:

TO-DO LIST

MY FAVORITE PART OF TODAY WAS:

WHAT I ATE TODAY:

BREAKFAST	LUNCH	DINNER

NOTES:

DON'T FORGET!

DAILY INSPIRATION:

"Science is organized knowledge. Wisdom is organized life."

-IMMANUEL KANT

PRODUCTIVITY SCORE FOR TODAY:

1 2 3 4 5 6 7 8 9 10

ENJOY TODAY

TODAY IS A GOOD DAY TO:

DATE: ____ / ____ / ____

MON TUE WED THU FRI SAT SUN

TODAY I AM FEELING:

THE WEATHER TODAY WAS:

TODAY I AM GRATEFUL FOR:

TO-DO LIST

MY FAVORITE PART OF TODAY WAS:

WHAT I ATE TODAY:

BREAKFAST	LUNCH	DINNER

NOTES:

DON'T FORGET!

DAILY INSPIRATION:

"A brother may not be a Friend,
but a Friend
will always be a brother."

-BENJAMIN FRANKLIN

PRODUCTIVITY SCORE FOR TODAY:

1 2 3 4 5 6 7 8 9 10

ENJOY TODAY

TODAY IS A GOOD DAY TO:

DATE: ____ / ____ / ____

MON TUE WED THU FRI SAT SUN

TODAY I AM FEELING:

THE WEATHER TODAY WAS:

TODAY I AM GRATEFUL FOR:

TO-DO LIST

MY FAVORITE PART OF TODAY WAS:

WHAT I ATE TODAY:

BREAKFAST	LUNCH	DINNER

NOTES:

DON'T FORGET!

DAILY INSPIRATION:

"Life is the art of drawing sufficient conclusions from insufficient premises."

-SAMUEL BUTLER

PRODUCTIVITY SCORE FOR TODAY:

1 2 3 4 5 6 7 8 9 10

Enjoy Today

TODAY IS A GOOD DAY TO:

DATE: ____ / ____ / ____

MON TUE WED THU FRI SAT SUN

TODAY I AM FEELING:

THE WEATHER TODAY WAS:

TODAY I AM GRATEFUL FOR:

TO-DO LIST

MY FAVORITE PART OF TODAY WAS:

WHAT I ATE TODAY:

BREAKFAST	LUNCH	DINNER

NOTES:

DON'T FORGET!

DAILY INSPIRATION:

"Leave no stone unturned."

-EURIPIDES

PRODUCTIVITY SCORE FOR TODAY:

1 2 3 4 5 6 7 8 9 10

ENJOY TODAY

TODAY IS A GOOD DAY TO:

DATE: ______ / ______ / ______

MON TUE WED THU FRI SAT SUN

TODAY I AM FEELING:

THE WEATHER TODAY WAS:

TODAY I AM GRATEFUL FOR:

TO-DO LIST

MY FAVORITE PART OF TODAY WAS:

WHAT I ATE TODAY:

BREAKFAST	LUNCH	DINNER

NOTES:

DON'T FORGET!

DAILY INSPIRATION:

"Love the sinner and hate the sin."

-SAINT AUGUSTINE OF HIPPO

PRODUCTIVITY SCORE FOR TODAY:

1 2 3 4 5 6 7 8 9 10

ENJOY TODAY

TODAY IS A GOOD DAY TO:

DATE: ______ / ______ / ______

MON TUE WED THU FRI SAT SUN

TODAY I AM FEELING:

THE WEATHER TODAY WAS:

TODAY I AM GRATEFUL FOR:

TO-DO LIST

MY FAVORITE PART OF TODAY WAS:

WHAT I ATE TODAY:

BREAKFAST	LUNCH	DINNER

NOTES:

DON'T FORGET!

DAILY INSPIRATION:

"The brave man carves out his fortune, and every man is the son of his own works."

-MIGUEL DE CERVANTES

PRODUCTIVITY SCORE FOR TODAY:

1 2 3 4 5 6 7 8 9 10

Enjoy Today

TODAY IS A GOOD DAY TO:

DATE: ______ / ______ / ______

MON TUE WED THU FRI SAT SUN

TODAY I AM FEELING:

THE WEATHER TODAY WAS:

TODAY I AM GRATEFUL FOR:

TO-DO LIST

MY FAVORITE PART OF TODAY WAS:

WHAT I ATE TODAY:

BREAKFAST	LUNCH	DINNER

NOTES:

DON'T FORGET!

DAILY INSPIRATION:

"Perfect happiness is keeping yourself alive, and only actionless action can have this effect."

–ZHUANGZI

PRODUCTIVITY SCORE FOR TODAY:

1 2 3 4 5 6 7 8 9 10

ENJOY TODAY

TODAY IS A GOOD DAY TO:

DATE: ____/____/____

MON TUE WED THU FRI SAT SUN

TODAY I AM FEELING:

THE WEATHER TODAY WAS:

TODAY I AM GRATEFUL FOR:

TO-DO LIST

MY FAVORITE PART OF TODAY WAS:

WHAT I ATE TODAY:

BREAKFAST	LUNCH	DINNER

NOTES:

DON'T FORGET!

DAILY INSPIRATION:

"Patience is the companion of wisdom."

-SAINT AUGUSTINE OF HIPPO

PRODUCTIVITY SCORE FOR TODAY:

1 2 3 4 5 6 7 8 9 10

Enjoy Today

TODAY IS A GOOD DAY TO:

DATE: ____ / ____ / ____

MON TUE WED THU FRI SAT SUN

TODAY I AM FEELING:

THE WEATHER TODAY WAS:

TODAY I AM GRATEFUL FOR:

TO-DO LIST

MY FAVORITE PART OF TODAY WAS:

WHAT I ATE TODAY:

BREAKFAST	LUNCH	DINNER

NOTES:

DON'T FORGET!

DAILY INSPIRATION:

"Every age has its pleasures, its style of wit, and its customs."

-NICOLAS BOILEAU-DESPRÉAUX

PRODUCTIVITY SCORE FOR TODAY:

1 2 3 4 5 6 7 8 9 10

ENJOY TODAY

TODAY IS A GOOD DAY TO:

DATE: ____ / ____ / ____

MON TUE WED THU FRI SAT SUN

TODAY I AM FEELING:

THE WEATHER TODAY WAS:

TODAY I AM GRATEFUL FOR:

TO-DO LIST

MY FAVORITE PART OF TODAY WAS:

WHAT I ATE TODAY:

BREAKFAST	LUNCH	DINNER

NOTES:

DON'T FORGET!

DAILY INSPIRATION:

"Seize the moments of happiness, love and be loved! That is the only reality in the world, all else is folly."

-LEO TOLSTOY

PRODUCTIVITY SCORE FOR TODAY:

1 2 3 4 5 6 7 8 9 10

TODAY IS A GOOD DAY TO:

DATE: ____ / ____ / ____

ENJOY TODAY

MON TUE WED THU FRI SAT SUN

TODAY I AM FEELING:

THE WEATHER TODAY WAS:

TODAY I AM GRATEFUL FOR:

TO-DO LIST

MY FAVORITE PART OF TODAY WAS:

WHAT I ATE TODAY:

BREAKFAST	LUNCH	DINNER

NOTES:

DON'T FORGET!

DAILY INSPIRATION:

"They who dream by day are cognizant of many things which escape those who dream only by night."

-EDGAR ALLAN POE

PRODUCTIVITY SCORE FOR TODAY:

1 2 3 4 5 6 7 8 9 10

ENJOY TODAY

TODAY IS A GOOD DAY TO:

DATE: ______ / ______ / ______

MON TUE WED THU FRI SAT SUN

TODAY I AM FEELING:

THE WEATHER TODAY WAS:

TODAY I AM GRATEFUL FOR:

TO-DO LIST

MY FAVORITE PART OF TODAY WAS:

WHAT I ATE TODAY:

BREAKFAST	LUNCH	DINNER

NOTES:

DON'T FORGET!

DAILY INSPIRATION:

"The universe is change: our life is what our thoughts make it."

-MARCUS AURELIUS

PRODUCTIVITY SCORE FOR TODAY:

1 2 3 4 5 6 7 8 9 10

ENJOY TODAY

TODAY IS A GOOD DAY TO:

DATE: ____/____/____

MON TUE WED THU FRI SAT SUN

TODAY I AM FEELING:

THE WEATHER TODAY WAS:

TODAY I AM GRATEFUL FOR:

TO-DO LIST

MY FAVORITE PART OF TODAY WAS:

WHAT I ATE TODAY:

BREAKFAST	LUNCH	DINNER

NOTES:

DON'T FORGET!

DAILY INSPIRATION:

"Accent is the soul of language; it gives to it both feeling and truth."

-JEAN-JACQUES ROUSSEAU

PRODUCTIVITY SCORE FOR TODAY:

1 2 3 4 5 6 7 8 9 10

ENJOY TODAY

TODAY IS A GOOD DAY TO:

DATE: ____ / ____ / ____

MON TUE WED THU FRI SAT SUN

TODAY I AM FEELING:

THE WEATHER TODAY WAS:

TODAY I AM GRATEFUL FOR:

TO-DO LIST

MY FAVORITE PART OF TODAY WAS:

WHAT I ATE TODAY:

BREAKFAST	LUNCH	DINNER

NOTES:

DON'T FORGET!

DAILY INSPIRATION:

"The very spring and root of honesty and virtue lie in good education."

-PLUTARCH

PRODUCTIVITY SCORE FOR TODAY:

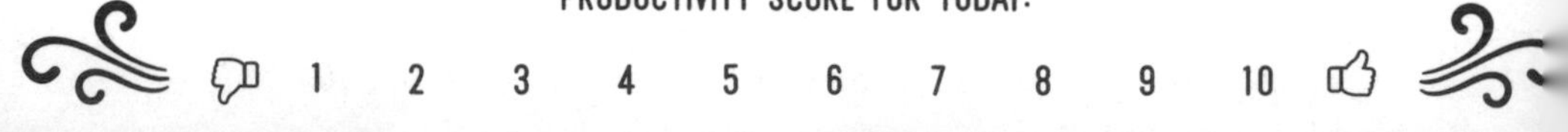

ENJOY TODAY

TODAY IS A GOOD DAY TO:

DATE: ____/____/____

MON TUE WED THU FRI SAT SUN

TODAY I AM FEELING:

THE WEATHER TODAY WAS:

TODAY I AM GRATEFUL FOR:

TO-DO LIST

MY FAVORITE PART OF TODAY WAS:

WHAT I ATE TODAY:

BREAKFAST	LUNCH	DINNER

NOTES:

DON'T FORGET!

DAILY INSPIRATION:

"Dignity does not consist in possessing honours, but in deserving them."

-ARISTOLE

PRODUCTIVITY SCORE FOR TODAY:

1 2 3 4 5 6 7 8 9 10

TODAY IS A GOOD DAY TO:

DATE: ____/____/____

MON TUE WED THU FRI SAT SUN

TODAY I AM FEELING:

THE WEATHER TODAY WAS:

TODAY I AM GRATEFUL FOR:

TO-DO LIST

MY FAVORITE PART OF TODAY WAS:

WHAT I ATE TODAY:

BREAKFAST	LUNCH	DINNER

NOTES:

DON'T FORGET!

DAILY INSPIRATION:

"Do not ask for what you will wish you had not got."

-LUCIUS ANNAEUS SENECA

PRODUCTIVITY SCORE FOR TODAY:

1 2 3 4 5 6 7 8 9 10

ENJOY TODAY

TODAY IS A GOOD DAY TO:

DATE: ____ / ____ / ____

MON TUE WED THU FRI SAT SUN

TODAY I AM FEELING:

THE WEATHER TODAY WAS:

TODAY I AM GRATEFUL FOR:

TO-DO LIST

MY FAVORITE PART OF TODAY WAS:

WHAT I ATE TODAY:

BREAKFAST	LUNCH	DINNER

NOTES:

DON'T FORGET!

DAILY INSPIRATION:

"Flattery won't hurt you if you don't swallow it."

-KIN HUBBARD

PRODUCTIVITY SCORE FOR TODAY:

1 2 3 4 5 6 7 8 9 10

ENJOY TODAY

TODAY IS A GOOD DAY TO:

DATE: ____ / ____ / ____

MON TUE WED THU FRI SAT SUN

TODAY I AM FEELING:

THE WEATHER TODAY WAS:

TODAY I AM GRATEFUL FOR:

TO-DO LIST

MY FAVORITE PART OF TODAY WAS:

WHAT I ATE TODAY:

BREAKFAST	LUNCH	DINNER

NOTES:

DON'T FORGET!

DAILY INSPIRATION:

"The most completely wasted of all days is that in which we have not laughed."

-NICOLAS CHAMFORT

PRODUCTIVITY SCORE FOR TODAY:

1 2 3 4 5 6 7 8 9 10

ENJOY TODAY

TODAY IS A GOOD DAY TO:

DATE: ____/____/____

MON TUE WED THU FRI SAT SUN

TODAY I AM FEELING:

THE WEATHER TODAY WAS:

TODAY I AM GRATEFUL FOR:

TO-DO LIST

MY FAVORITE PART OF TODAY WAS:

WHAT I ATE TODAY:

BREAKFAST	LUNCH	DINNER

NOTES:

DON'T FORGET!

DAILY INSPIRATION:

"We have two ears and one mouth, so we should listen more than we say."

-ZENO OF CITIUM

PRODUCTIVITY SCORE FOR TODAY:

1 2 3 4 5 6 7 8 9 10

ENJOY TODAY

TODAY IS A GOOD DAY TO:

DATE: ______ / ______ / ______

MON TUE WED THU FRI SAT SUN

TODAY I AM FEELING:

THE WEATHER TODAY WAS:

TODAY I AM GRATEFUL FOR:

TO-DO LIST

MY FAVORITE PART OF TODAY WAS:

WHAT I ATE TODAY:

BREAKFAST	LUNCH	DINNER

NOTES:

DON'T FORGET!

DAILY INSPIRATION:

"Every man is a new method."

-RALPH WALDO EMERSON

PRODUCTIVITY SCORE FOR TODAY:

1 2 3 4 5 6 7 8 9 10

ENJOY TODAY

TODAY IS A GOOD DAY TO:

DATE: ____ / ____ / ____

MON TUE WED THU FRI SAT SUN

TODAY I AM FEELING:

THE WEATHER TODAY WAS:

TODAY I AM GRATEFUL FOR:

TO-DO LIST

MY FAVORITE PART OF TODAY WAS:

WHAT I ATE TODAY:

BREAKFAST	LUNCH	DINNER

NOTES:

DON'T FORGET!

DAILY INSPIRATION:

"Love does not dominate, it cultivates. And that is more."

–JOHANN WOLFGANG VON GOETHE

PRODUCTIVITY SCORE FOR TODAY:

1 2 3 4 5 6 7 8 9 10

ENJOY TODAY

TODAY IS A GOOD DAY TO:

DATE: ____/____/____

MON TUE WED THU FRI SAT SUN

TODAY I AM FEELING:

THE WEATHER TODAY WAS:

TODAY I AM GRATEFUL FOR:

TO-DO LIST

MY FAVORITE PART OF TODAY WAS:

WHAT I ATE TODAY:

BREAKFAST	LUNCH	DINNER

NOTES:

DON'T FORGET!

DAILY INSPIRATION:

"When lost in a forest go always down hill. When lost in a philosophy or doctrine go upward."

-AMBROSE BIERCE

PRODUCTIVITY SCORE FOR TODAY:

1 2 3 4 5 6 7 8 9 10

ENJOY TODAY

ODAY IS A GOOD DAY TO:

DATE: ______ / ______ / ______

MON TUE WED THU FRI SAT SUN

ODAY I AM FEELING:

THE WEATHER TODAY WAS:

ODAY I AM GRATEFUL FOR:

TO-DO LIST

Y FAVORITE PART OF TODAY WAS:

HAT I ATE TODAY:

BREAKFAST	LUNCH	DINNER

OTES:

DON'T FORGET!

DAILY INSPIRATION:

"The fool doth think he is wise, but the wise man knows himself to be a fool."

-WILLIAM SHAKESPEARE

PRODUCTIVITY SCORE FOR TODAY:

1 2 3 4 5 6 7 8 9 10

Enjoy Today

TODAY IS A GOOD DAY TO:

DATE: _____ / _____ / _____

MON TUE WED THU FRI SAT SUN

TODAY I AM FEELING:

THE WEATHER TODAY WAS:

TODAY I AM GRATEFUL FOR:

TO-DO LIST

MY FAVORITE PART OF TODAY WAS:

WHAT I ATE TODAY:

BREAKFAST	LUNCH	DINNER

NOTES:

DON'T FORGET!

DAILY INSPIRATION:

"Age is never so old as youth would measure it."

-JACK LONDON

PRODUCTIVITY SCORE FOR TODAY:

ENJOY TODAY

TODAY IS A GOOD DAY TO:

DATE: ____ / ____ / ____

MON TUE WED THU FRI SAT SUN

TODAY I AM FEELING:

THE WEATHER TODAY WAS:

TODAY I AM GRATEFUL FOR:

TO-DO LIST

MY FAVORITE PART OF TODAY WAS:

WHAT I ATE TODAY:

BREAKFAST	LUNCH	DINNER

NOTES:

DON'T FORGET!

DAILY INSPIRATION:

"What does not kill me, makes me stronger."

-FRIEDRICH NIETZSCHE

PRODUCTIVITY SCORE FOR TODAY:

1 2 3 4 5 6 7 8 9 10

ENJOY TODAY

TODAY IS A GOOD DAY TO:

DATE: ______ / ______ / ______

MON TUE WED THU FRI SAT SUN

TODAY I AM FEELING:

THE WEATHER TODAY WAS:

TODAY I AM GRATEFUL FOR:

TO-DO LIST

MY FAVORITE PART OF TODAY WAS:

WHAT I ATE TODAY:

BREAKFAST	LUNCH	DINNER

NOTES:

DON'T FORGET!

DAILY INSPIRATION:

"Each of us inevitable; Each of us limitless—each of us with his or her right upon the earth."

-WALT WHITMAN

PRODUCTIVITY SCORE FOR TODAY:

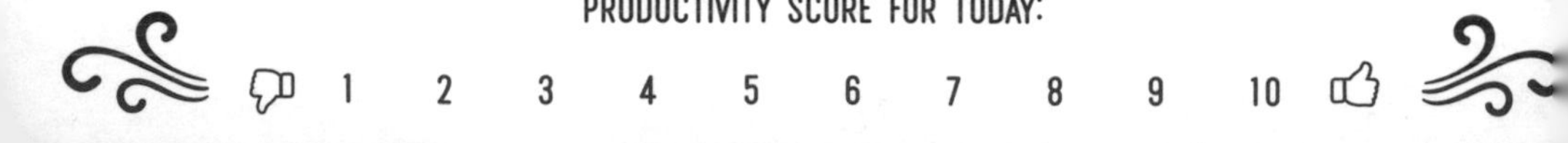

ENJOY TODAY

TODAY IS A GOOD DAY TO:

DATE: ____ / ____ / ____

MON TUE WED THU FRI SAT SUN

TODAY I AM FEELING:

THE WEATHER TODAY WAS:

TODAY I AM GRATEFUL FOR:

TO-DO LIST

MY FAVORITE PART OF TODAY WAS:

WHAT I ATE TODAY:

BREAKFAST	LUNCH	DINNER

NOTES:

DON'T FORGET!

DAILY INSPIRATION:

"For the strength of the Pack is the Wolf, and the strength of the Wolf is the Pack."

-RUDYARD KIPLING

PRODUCTIVITY SCORE FOR TODAY:

1 2 3 4 5 6 7 8 9 10

ENJOY TODAY

TODAY IS A GOOD DAY TO:

DATE: ______ / ______ / ______

MON TUE WED THU FRI SAT SUN

TODAY I AM FEELING:

THE WEATHER TODAY WAS:

TODAY I AM GRATEFUL FOR:

TO-DO LIST

MY FAVORITE PART OF TODAY WAS:

WHAT I ATE TODAY:

BREAKFAST	LUNCH	DINNER

NOTES:

DON'T FORGET!

DAILY INSPIRATION:

"No limits but the sky."

-MIGUEL DE CERVANTES

PRODUCTIVITY SCORE FOR TODAY:

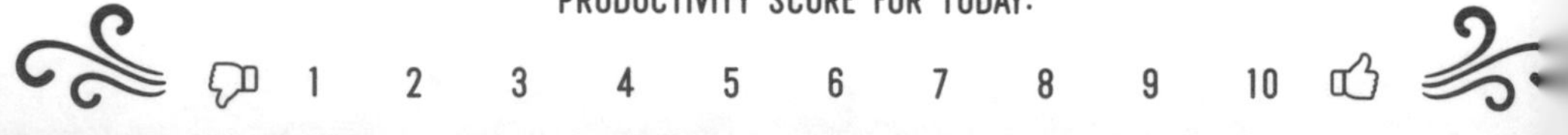

ENJOY TODAY

TODAY IS A GOOD DAY TO:

DATE: ____ / ____ / ____

MON TUE WED THU FRI SAT SUN

TODAY I AM FEELING:

THE WEATHER TODAY WAS:

TODAY I AM GRATEFUL FOR:

TO-DO LIST

MY FAVORITE PART OF TODAY WAS:

WHAT I ATE TODAY:

BREAKFAST	LUNCH	DINNER

NOTES:

DON'T FORGET!

DAILY INSPIRATION:

"The imagination is the eye of the soul."

-JOSEPH JOUBERT

PRODUCTIVITY SCORE FOR TODAY:

1 2 3 4 5 6 7 8 9 10

ENJOY TODAY

TODAY IS A GOOD DAY TO:

DATE: ____ / ____ / ____

MON TUE WED THU FRI SAT SUN

TODAY I AM FEELING:

THE WEATHER TODAY WAS:

TODAY I AM GRATEFUL FOR:

TO-DO LIST

MY FAVORITE PART OF TODAY WAS:

WHAT I ATE TODAY:

BREAKFAST	LUNCH	DINNER

NOTES:

DON'T FORGET!

DAILY INSPIRATION:

"Dreams seem to be spurred on not by reason but by desire, not by the head but by the heart..."

-FYODOR DOSTOYEVSKY

PRODUCTIVITY SCORE FOR TODAY:

1 2 3 4 5 6 7 8 9 10

ENJOY TODAY

TODAY IS A GOOD DAY TO:

DATE: ____ / ____ / ____

MON TUE WED THU FRI SAT SUN

TODAY I AM FEELING:

THE WEATHER TODAY WAS:

TODAY I AM GRATEFUL FOR:

TO-DO LIST

MY FAVORITE PART OF TODAY WAS:

WHAT I ATE TODAY:

BREAKFAST	LUNCH	DINNER

NOTES:

DON'T FORGET!

DAILY INSPIRATION:

"No man is happy without a delusion of some kind. Delusions are as necessary to our happiness as realities."

-CHRISTIAN NESTELL BOVEE

PRODUCTIVITY SCORE FOR TODAY:

1 2 3 4 5 6 7 8 9 10

Enjoy Today

TODAY IS A GOOD DAY TO:

DATE: ______ / ______ / ______

MON TUE WED THU FRI SAT SUN

TODAY I AM FEELING:

THE WEATHER TODAY WAS:

TODAY I AM GRATEFUL FOR:

TO-DO LIST

MY FAVORITE PART OF TODAY WAS:

WHAT I ATE TODAY:

BREAKFAST	LUNCH	DINNER

NOTES:

DON'T FORGET!

DAILY INSPIRATION:

"In life, as in chess, forethought wins."

-CHARLES BUXTON

PRODUCTIVITY SCORE FOR TODAY:

1 2 3 4 5 6 7 8 9 10

ENJOY TODAY

TODAY IS A GOOD DAY TO:

DATE: ____ / ____ / ____

MON TUE WED THU FRI SAT SUN

TODAY I AM FEELING:

THE WEATHER TODAY WAS:

TODAY I AM GRATEFUL FOR:

TO-DO LIST

MY FAVORITE PART OF TODAY WAS:

WHAT I ATE TODAY:

BREAKFAST	LUNCH	DINNER

NOTES:

DON'T FORGET!

DAILY INSPIRATION:

"A well-written life is almost as rare as a well-spent one."

-THOMAS CARLYLE

PRODUCTIVITY SCORE FOR TODAY:

1 2 3 4 5 6 7 8 9 10

ENJOY TODAY

TODAY IS A GOOD DAY TO:

DATE: ____/____/____

MON TUE WED THU FRI SAT SUN

TODAY I AM FEELING:

THE WEATHER TODAY WAS:

TODAY I AM GRATEFUL FOR:

TO-DO LIST

MY FAVORITE PART OF TODAY WAS:

WHAT I ATE TODAY:

BREAKFAST	LUNCH	DINNER

NOTES:

DON'T FORGET!

DAILY INSPIRATION:

"If everything were excellent here below, nothing would stand out as excellent."

-DENIS DIDEROT

PRODUCTIVITY SCORE FOR TODAY:

1 2 3 4 5 6 7 8 9 10

ENJOY TODAY

TODAY IS A GOOD DAY TO:

DATE: ____/____/____

MON TUE WED THU FRI SAT SUN

TODAY I AM FEELING:

THE WEATHER TODAY WAS:

TODAY I AM GRATEFUL FOR:

TO-DO LIST

MY FAVORITE PART OF TODAY WAS:

WHAT I ATE TODAY:

BREAKFAST	LUNCH	DINNER

NOTES:

DON'T FORGET!

DAILY INSPIRATION:

"Practice yourself, for heaven's sake, in little things; and thence proceed to greater."

-EPICTETUS

PRODUCTIVITY SCORE FOR TODAY:

1 2 3 4 5 6 7 8 9 10

ENJOY TODAY

TODAY IS A GOOD DAY TO:

DATE: ______ / ______ / ______

MON TUE WED THU FRI SAT SUN

TODAY I AM FEELING:

THE WEATHER TODAY WAS:

TODAY I AM GRATEFUL FOR:

TO-DO LIST

MY FAVORITE PART OF TODAY WAS:

WHAT I ATE TODAY:

BREAKFAST	LUNCH	DINNER

NOTES:

DON'T FORGET!

DAILY INSPIRATION:

"He who is not satisfied with a little, is satisfied with nothing."

-EPICURUS

PRODUCTIVITY SCORE FOR TODAY:

1 2 3 4 5 6 7 8 9 10

ENJOY TODAY

TODAY IS A GOOD DAY TO:

DATE: ____/____/____

MON TUE WED THU FRI SAT SUN

TODAY I AM FEELING:

THE WEATHER TODAY WAS:

TODAY I AM GRATEFUL FOR:

TO-DO LIST

MY FAVORITE PART OF TODAY WAS:

WHAT I ATE TODAY:

BREAKFAST	LUNCH	DINNER

NOTES:

DON'T FORGET!

DAILY INSPIRATION:

"The beginnings of all things are small."

-MARCUS TULLIUS CICERO

PRODUCTIVITY SCORE FOR TODAY:

1 2 3 4 5 6 7 8 9 10

ENJOY TODAY

TODAY IS A GOOD DAY TO:

DATE: ____/____/____

MON TUE WED THU FRI SAT SUN

TODAY I AM FEELING:

THE WEATHER TODAY WAS:

TODAY I AM GRATEFUL FOR:

TO-DO LIST

MY FAVORITE PART OF TODAY WAS:

WHAT I ATE TODAY:

BREAKFAST	LUNCH	DINNER

NOTES:

DON'T FORGET!

DAILY INSPIRATION:

"One never notices what has been done; one can only see what remains to be done."

-MARIE CURIE

PRODUCTIVITY SCORE FOR TODAY:

1 2 3 4 5 6 7 8 9 10

ENJOY TODAY

TODAY IS A GOOD DAY TO:

DATE: ___ / ___ / ___

MON TUE WED THU FRI SAT SUN

TODAY I AM FEELING:

THE WEATHER TODAY WAS:

TODAY I AM GRATEFUL FOR:

TO-DO LIST

MY FAVORITE PART OF TODAY WAS:

WHAT I ATE TODAY:

BREAKFAST	LUNCH	DINNER

NOTES:

DON'T FORGET!

DAILY INSPIRATION:

"The man who never alters his opinion is like standing water, and breeds reptiles of the mind."

-WILLIAM BLAKE

PRODUCTIVITY SCORE FOR TODAY:

1 2 3 4 5 6 7 8 9 10

ENJOY TODAY

TODAY IS A GOOD DAY TO:

DATE: ____ / ____ / ____

MON TUE WED THU FRI SAT SUN

TODAY I AM FEELING:

THE WEATHER TODAY WAS:

TODAY I AM GRATEFUL FOR:

TO-DO LIST

MY FAVORITE PART OF TODAY WAS:

WHAT I ATE TODAY:

BREAKFAST	LUNCH	DINNER

NOTES:

DON'T FORGET!

DAILY INSPIRATION:

"If you want to be loved, be lovable."

-OVID

PRODUCTIVITY SCORE FOR TODAY:

1 2 3 4 5 6 7 8 9 10

ODAY IS A GOOD DAY TO:

DATE: ______ / ______ / ______

ENJOY TODAY

MON TUE WED THU FRI SAT SUN

ODAY I AM FEELING:

THE WEATHER TODAY WAS:

ODAY I AM GRATEFUL FOR:

TO-DO LIST

Y FAVORITE PART OF TODAY WAS:

HAT I ATE TODAY:

BREAKFAST	LUNCH	DINNER

OTES:

DON'T FORGET!

DAILY INSPIRATION:

"Practice and thought might gradually forge many an art."

-VIRGIL

PRODUCTIVITY SCORE FOR TODAY:

1 2 3 4 5 6 7 8 9 10

ENJOY TODAY

TODAY IS A GOOD DAY TO:

DATE: ____/____/____

MON TUE WED THU FRI SAT SUN

TODAY I AM FEELING:

THE WEATHER TODAY WAS:

TODAY I AM GRATEFUL FOR:

TO-DO LIST

MY FAVORITE PART OF TODAY WAS:

WHAT I ATE TODAY:

BREAKFAST	LUNCH	DINNER

NOTES:

DON'T FORGET!

DAILY INSPIRATION:

"Do not fear mistakes. You will know failure. Continue to reach out."

-BENJAMIN FRANKLIN

PRODUCTIVITY SCORE FOR TODAY:

1 2 3 4 5 6 7 8 9 10

Enjoy Today

TODAY IS A GOOD DAY TO:

DATE: ____ / ____ / ____

MON TUE WED THU FRI SAT SUN

TODAY I AM FEELING:

THE WEATHER TODAY WAS:

TODAY I AM GRATEFUL FOR:

TO-DO LIST

MY FAVORITE PART OF TODAY WAS:

WHAT I ATE TODAY:

BREAKFAST	LUNCH	DINNER

NOTES:

DON'T FORGET!

DAILY INSPIRATION:

"First say to yourself what you would be; and then do what you have to do."

-EPICTETUS

PRODUCTIVITY SCORE FOR TODAY:

1 2 3 4 5 6 7 8 9 10

ENJOY TODAY

TODAY IS A GOOD DAY TO:

DATE: ______ / ______ / ______

MON TUE WED THU FRI SAT SUN

TODAY I AM FEELING:

THE WEATHER TODAY WAS:

TODAY I AM GRATEFUL FOR:

TO-DO LIST

MY FAVORITE PART OF TODAY WAS:

WHAT I ATE TODAY:

BREAKFAST	LUNCH	DINNER

NOTES:

DON'T FORGET!

DAILY INSPIRATION:

"There is no foreign land; it is the traveller only that is foreign."

-ROBERT LOUIS STEVENSON

PRODUCTIVITY SCORE FOR TODAY:

ENJOY TODAY

TODAY IS A GOOD DAY TO:

DATE: ____/____/____

MON TUE WED THU FRI SAT SUN

TODAY I AM FEELING:

THE WEATHER TODAY WAS:

TODAY I AM GRATEFUL FOR:

TO-DO LIST

MY FAVORITE PART OF TODAY WAS:

WHAT I ATE TODAY:

BREAKFAST	LUNCH	DINNER

NOTES:

DON'T FORGET!

DAILY INSPIRATION:

"Man is free at the instant he wants to be."

-VOLTAIRE

PRODUCTIVITY SCORE FOR TODAY:

1 2 3 4 5 6 7 8 9 10

Enjoy Today

TODAY IS A GOOD DAY TO:

DATE: ____ / ____ / ____

MON TUE WED THU FRI SAT SUN

TODAY I AM FEELING:

THE WEATHER TODAY WAS:

TODAY I AM GRATEFUL FOR:

TO-DO LIST

MY FAVORITE PART OF TODAY WAS:

WHAT I ATE TODAY:

BREAKFAST	LUNCH	DINNER

NOTES:

DON'T FORGET!

DAILY INSPIRATION:

"In matters of style, swim with the current; in matters of principle, stand like a rock."

-THOMAS JEFFERSON

PRODUCTIVITY SCORE FOR TODAY:

1 2 3 4 5 6 7 8 9 10

ENJOY TODAY

TODAY IS A GOOD DAY TO:

DATE: ____/____/____

MON TUE WED THU FRI SAT SUN

TODAY I AM FEELING:

THE WEATHER TODAY WAS:

TODAY I AM GRATEFUL FOR:

TO-DO LIST

MY FAVORITE PART OF TODAY WAS:

WHAT I ATE TODAY:

BREAKFAST	LUNCH	DINNER

NOTES:

DON'T FORGET!

DAILY INSPIRATION:

"Virtue and vice are not the same, even if they undergo the same torment."

-SAINT AUGUSTINE OF HIPPO

PRODUCTIVITY SCORE FOR TODAY:

1 2 3 4 5 6 7 8 9 10

Enjoy Today

TODAY IS A GOOD DAY TO:

DATE: ____/____/____

MON TUE WED THU FRI SAT SUN

TODAY I AM FEELING:

THE WEATHER TODAY WAS:

TODAY I AM GRATEFUL FOR:

TO-DO LIST

MY FAVORITE PART OF TODAY WAS:

WHAT I ATE TODAY:

BREAKFAST	LUNCH	DINNER

NOTES:

DON'T FORGET!

DAILY INSPIRATION:

"We grow great by dreams."

-WOODROW WILSON

PRODUCTIVITY SCORE FOR TODAY:

1 2 3 4 5 6 7 8 9 10

ENJOY TODAY

TODAY IS A GOOD DAY TO:

DATE: ____ / ____ / ____

MON TUE WED THU FRI SAT SUN

TODAY I AM FEELING:

THE WEATHER TODAY WAS:

TODAY I AM GRATEFUL FOR:

TO-DO LIST

MY FAVORITE PART OF TODAY WAS:

WHAT I ATE TODAY:

BREAKFAST	LUNCH	DINNER

NOTES:

DON'T FORGET!

DAILY INSPIRATION:

"Change alone is eternal, perpetual, immortal."

-ARTHUR SCHOPENHAUER

PRODUCTIVITY SCORE FOR TODAY:

1 2 3 4 5 6 7 8 9 10

ENJOY TODAY

TODAY IS A GOOD DAY TO:

DATE: ____ / ____ / ____

MON TUE WED THU FRI SAT SUN

TODAY I AM FEELING:

THE WEATHER TODAY WAS:

TODAY I AM GRATEFUL FOR:

TO-DO LIST

MY FAVORITE PART OF TODAY WAS:

WHAT I ATE TODAY:

BREAKFAST	LUNCH	DINNER

NOTES:

DON'T FORGET!

DAILY INSPIRATION:

"When work is a pleasure,
life is a joy.
When work is duty,
life is slavery."

-MAXIM GORKY

PRODUCTIVITY SCORE FOR TODAY:

1 2 3 4 5 6 7 8 9 10

ENJOY TODAY

TODAY IS A GOOD DAY TO:

DATE: ____ / ____ / ____

MON TUE WED THU FRI SAT SUN

TODAY I AM FEELING:

THE WEATHER TODAY WAS:

TODAY I AM GRATEFUL FOR:

TO-DO LIST

MY FAVORITE PART OF TODAY WAS:

WHAT I ATE TODAY:

BREAKFAST	LUNCH	DINNER

NOTES:

DON'T FORGET!

DAILY INSPIRATION:

"Major achievements are less often the result of a single great effort than from the accumulation of several smaller ones."

-GUSTAVE LE BON

PRODUCTIVITY SCORE FOR TODAY:

1 2 3 4 5 6 7 8 9 10

ENJOY TODAY

TODAY IS A GOOD DAY TO:

DATE: ____ / ____ / ____

MON TUE WED THU FRI SAT SUN

TODAY I AM FEELING:

THE WEATHER TODAY WAS:

TODAY I AM GRATEFUL FOR:

TO-DO LIST

MY FAVORITE PART OF TODAY WAS:

WHAT I ATE TODAY:

BREAKFAST	LUNCH	DINNER

NOTES:

DON'T FORGET!

DAILY INSPIRATION:

"Once we know our weaknesses they cease to do us any harm."

-GEORG C. LICHTENBERG

PRODUCTIVITY SCORE FOR TODAY:

1 2 3 4 5 6 7 8 9 10

ENJOY TODAY

TODAY IS A GOOD DAY TO:

DATE: ____ / ____ / ____

MON TUE WED THU FRI SAT SUN

TODAY I AM FEELING:

THE WEATHER TODAY WAS:

TODAY I AM GRATEFUL FOR:

TO-DO LIST

MY FAVORITE PART OF TODAY WAS:

WHAT I ATE TODAY:

BREAKFAST	LUNCH	DINNER

NOTES:

DON'T FORGET!

DAILY INSPIRATION:

"You could not step twice into the same river."

—HERACLITUS

PRODUCTIVITY SCORE FOR TODAY:

1 2 3 4 5 6 7 8 9 10

ENJOY TODAY

TODAY IS A GOOD DAY TO:

DATE: ______ / ______ / ______

MON TUE WED THU FRI SAT SUN

TODAY I AM FEELING:

THE WEATHER TODAY WAS:

TODAY I AM GRATEFUL FOR:

TO-DO LIST

MY FAVORITE PART OF TODAY WAS:

WHAT I ATE TODAY:

BREAKFAST	LUNCH	DINNER

NOTES:

DON'T FORGET!

DAILY INSPIRATION:

"Have nothing in your house that you do not know to be useful, or believe to be beautiful."

-WILLIAM MORRIS

PRODUCTIVITY SCORE FOR TODAY:

1 2 3 4 5 6 7 8 9 10

ENJOY TODAY

TODAY IS A GOOD DAY TO:

DATE: ____ / ____ / ____

MON TUE WED THU FRI SAT SUN

TODAY I AM FEELING:

THE WEATHER TODAY WAS:

TODAY I AM GRATEFUL FOR:

TO-DO LIST

MY FAVORITE PART OF TODAY WAS:

WHAT I ATE TODAY:

BREAKFAST	LUNCH	DINNER

NOTES:

DON'T FORGET!

DAILY INSPIRATION:

"If I have a thousand ideas and only one turns out to be good, I am satisfied."

-ALFRED NOBEL

PRODUCTIVITY SCORE FOR TODAY:

1 2 3 4 5 6 7 8 9 10

Enjoy Today

TODAY IS A GOOD DAY TO:

DATE: ____ / ____ / ____

MON TUE WED THU FRI SAT SUN

TODAY I AM FEELING:

THE WEATHER TODAY WAS:

TODAY I AM GRATEFUL FOR:

TO-DO LIST

MY FAVORITE PART OF TODAY WAS:

WHAT I ATE TODAY:

BREAKFAST	LUNCH	DINNER

NOTES:

DON'T FORGET!

DAILY INSPIRATION:

"In most cases men willingly believe what they wish."

-JULIUS CAESAR

PRODUCTIVITY SCORE FOR TODAY:

1 2 3 4 5 6 7 8 9 10

ENJOY TODAY

TODAY IS A GOOD DAY TO:

DATE: ____ / ____ / ____

MON TUE WED THU FRI SAT SUN

TODAY I AM FEELING:

THE WEATHER TODAY WAS:

TODAY I AM GRATEFUL FOR:

TO-DO LIST

MY FAVORITE PART OF TODAY WAS:

WHAT I ATE TODAY:

BREAKFAST	LUNCH	DINNER

NOTES:

DON'T FORGET!

DAILY INSPIRATION:

"Nothing ever becomes real till it is experienced."

-JOHN KEATS

PRODUCTIVITY SCORE FOR TODAY:

1 2 3 4 5 6 7 8 9 10

Enjoy Today

TODAY IS A GOOD DAY TO:

DATE: ____ / ____ / ____

MON TUE WED THU FRI SAT SUN

TODAY I AM FEELING:

THE WEATHER TODAY WAS:

TODAY I AM GRATEFUL FOR:

TO-DO LIST

MY FAVORITE PART OF TODAY WAS:

WHAT I ATE TODAY:

BREAKFAST	LUNCH	DINNER

NOTES:

DON'T FORGET!

DAILY INSPIRATION:

"Don't be afraid of opposition. Remember, a kite rises against, not with, the wind."

-HAMILTON MABIE

PRODUCTIVITY SCORE FOR TODAY:

1 2 3 4 5 6 7 8 9 10

ENJOY TODAY

TODAY IS A GOOD DAY TO:

DATE: ____ / ____ / ____

MON TUE WED THU FRI SAT SUN

TODAY I AM FEELING:

THE WEATHER TODAY WAS:

TODAY I AM GRATEFUL FOR:

TO-DO LIST

MY FAVORITE PART OF TODAY WAS:

WHAT I ATE TODAY:

BREAKFAST	LUNCH	DINNER

NOTES:

DON'T FORGET!

DAILY INSPIRATION:

"Perseverance is not a long race; it is many short races one after another."

-WALTER ELLIOTT

PRODUCTIVITY SCORE FOR TODAY:

1 2 3 4 5 6 7 8 9 10

Enjoy Today

TODAY IS A GOOD DAY TO:

DATE: ____ / ____ / ____

MON TUE WED THU FRI SAT SUN

TODAY I AM FEELING:

THE WEATHER TODAY WAS:

TODAY I AM GRATEFUL FOR:

TO-DO LIST

MY FAVORITE PART OF TODAY WAS:

WHAT I ATE TODAY:

BREAKFAST	LUNCH	DINNER

NOTES:

DON'T FORGET!

DAILY INSPIRATION:

"Be pitiful, for every man is fighting a hard battle."

-IAN MACLAREN

PRODUCTIVITY SCORE FOR TODAY:

1 2 3 4 5 6 7 8 9 10

ENJOY TODAY

TODAY IS A GOOD DAY TO:

DATE: ______ / ______ / ______

MON TUE WED THU FRI SAT SUN

TODAY I AM FEELING:

THE WEATHER TODAY WAS:

TODAY I AM GRATEFUL FOR:

TO-DO LIST

MY FAVORITE PART OF TODAY WAS:

WHAT I ATE TODAY:

BREAKFAST	LUNCH	DINNER

NOTES:

DON'T FORGET!

DAILY INSPIRATION:

"Nothing succeeds like success."

-ALEXANDRE DUMAS

PRODUCTIVITY SCORE FOR TODAY:

1 2 3 4 5 6 7 8 9 10

ENJOY TODAY

TODAY IS A GOOD DAY TO:

DATE: ______ / ______ / ______

MON TUE WED THU FRI SAT SUN

TODAY I AM FEELING:

THE WEATHER TODAY WAS:

TODAY I AM GRATEFUL FOR:

TO-DO LIST

MY FAVORITE PART OF TODAY WAS:

WHAT I ATE TODAY:

BREAKFAST	LUNCH	DINNER

NOTES:

DON'T FORGET!

DAILY INSPIRATION:

"If I have seen further it is only by standing on the shoulder of giants."

-ISAAC NEWTON

PRODUCTIVITY SCORE FOR TODAY:

1 2 3 4 5 6 7 8 9 10

ENJOY TODAY

TODAY IS A GOOD DAY TO:

DATE: ____ / ____ / ____

MON TUE WED THU FRI SAT SUN

TODAY I AM FEELING:

THE WEATHER TODAY WAS:

TODAY I AM GRATEFUL FOR:

TO-DO LIST

MY FAVORITE PART OF TODAY WAS:

WHAT I ATE TODAY:

BREAKFAST	LUNCH	DINNER

NOTES:

DON'T FORGET!

DAILY INSPIRATION:

"To study and not think is a waste. To think and not study is dangerous."

-CONFUCIUS

PRODUCTIVITY SCORE FOR TODAY:

1 2 3 4 5 6 7 8 9 10

ENJOY TODAY

TODAY IS A GOOD DAY TO:

DATE: ____ / ____ / ____

MON TUE WED THU FRI SAT SUN

TODAY I AM FEELING:

THE WEATHER TODAY WAS:

TODAY I AM GRATEFUL FOR:

TO-DO LIST

MY FAVORITE PART OF TODAY WAS:

WHAT I ATE TODAY:

BREAKFAST	LUNCH	DINNER

NOTES:

DON'T FORGET!

DAILY INSPIRATION:

"The art of life is to know how to enjoy a little and to endure a lot."

-WILLIAM HAZLITT

PRODUCTIVITY SCORE FOR TODAY:

1 2 3 4 5 6 7 8 9 10

ENJOY TODAY

TODAY IS A GOOD DAY TO:

DATE: ____ / ____ / ____

MON TUE WED THU FRI SAT SUN

TODAY I AM FEELING:

THE WEATHER TODAY WAS:

TODAY I AM GRATEFUL FOR:

TO-DO LIST

MY FAVORITE PART OF TODAY WAS:

WHAT I ATE TODAY:

BREAKFAST	LUNCH	DINNER

NOTES:

DON'T FORGET!

DAILY INSPIRATION:

"Man is never perfect, nor contented."

-JULES VERNE

PRODUCTIVITY SCORE FOR TODAY:

1 2 3 4 5 6 7 8 9 10

Enjoy Today

TODAY IS A GOOD DAY TO:

DATE: ____ / ____ / ____

MON TUE WED THU FRI SAT SUN

TODAY I AM FEELING:

THE WEATHER TODAY WAS:

TODAY I AM GRATEFUL FOR:

TO-DO LIST

MY FAVORITE PART OF TODAY WAS:

WHAT I ATE TODAY:

BREAKFAST	LUNCH	DINNER

NOTES:

DON'T FORGET!

DAILY INSPIRATION:

"For the things we have to learn before we can do, we learn by doing."

-ARISTOTLE

PRODUCTIVITY SCORE FOR TODAY:

1 2 3 4 5 6 7 8 9 10

ENJOY TODAY

TODAY IS A GOOD DAY TO:

DATE: ____/____/____

MON TUE WED THU FRI SAT SUN

TODAY I AM FEELING:

THE WEATHER TODAY WAS:

TODAY I AM GRATEFUL FOR:

TO-DO LIST

MY FAVORITE PART OF TODAY WAS:

WHAT I ATE TODAY:

BREAKFAST	LUNCH	DINNER

NOTES:

DON'T FORGET!

DAILY INSPIRATION:

"Happiness is beneficial for the body but it is grief that develops the powers of the mind."

-MARCEL PROUST

PRODUCTIVITY SCORE FOR TODAY:

1 2 3 4 5 6 7 8 9 10

ENJOY TODAY

TODAY IS A GOOD DAY TO:

DATE: ____ / ____ / ____

MON TUE WED THU FRI SAT SUN

TODAY I AM FEELING:

THE WEATHER TODAY WAS:

TODAY I AM GRATEFUL FOR:

TO-DO LIST

MY FAVORITE PART OF TODAY WAS:

WHAT I ATE TODAY:

BREAKFAST	LUNCH	DINNER

NOTES:

DON'T FORGET!

DAILY INSPIRATION:

"An honest man nearly always thinks justly."

-JEAN-JACQUES ROUSSEAU

PRODUCTIVITY SCORE FOR TODAY:

1 2 3 4 5 6 7 8 9 10

ENJOY TODAY

TODAY IS A GOOD DAY TO:

DATE: ____ / ____ / ____

MON TUE WED THU FRI SAT SUN

TODAY I AM FEELING:

THE WEATHER TODAY WAS:

TODAY I AM GRATEFUL FOR:

TO-DO LIST

MY FAVORITE PART OF TODAY WAS:

WHAT I ATE TODAY:

BREAKFAST	LUNCH	DINNER

NOTES:

DON'T FORGET!

DAILY INSPIRATION:

"The most effective way to do it, is to do it."

-AMELIA EARHART

PRODUCTIVITY SCORE FOR TODAY:

1 2 3 4 5 6 7 8 9 10

ENJOY TODAY

TODAY IS A GOOD DAY TO:

DATE: ____ / ____ / ____

MON TUE WED THU FRI SAT SUN

TODAY I AM FEELING:

THE WEATHER TODAY WAS:

TODAY I AM GRATEFUL FOR:

TO-DO LIST

MY FAVORITE PART OF TODAY WAS:

WHAT I ATE TODAY:

BREAKFAST	LUNCH	DINNER

NOTES:

DON'T FORGET!

DAILY INSPIRATION:

"The greatness of human actions is measured by the inspirations that initiated them."

-LOUIS PASTEUR

PRODUCTIVITY SCORE FOR TODAY:

1 2 3 4 5 6 7 8 9 10

ENJOY TODAY

TODAY IS A GOOD DAY TO:

DATE: ____/____/____

MON TUE WED THU FRI SAT SUN

TODAY I AM FEELING:

THE WEATHER TODAY WAS:

TODAY I AM GRATEFUL FOR:

TO-DO LIST

MY FAVORITE PART OF TODAY WAS:

WHAT I ATE TODAY:

BREAKFAST	LUNCH	DINNER

NOTES:

DON'T FORGET!

DAILY INSPIRATION:

"Happiness is not an end—
it is only a means,
and adjunct, a consequence."

—DINAH CRAIK

PRODUCTIVITY SCORE FOR TODAY:

1 2 3 4 5 6 7 8 9 10

ENJOY TODAY

TODAY IS A GOOD DAY TO:

DATE: ______ / ______ / ______

MON TUE WED THU FRI SAT SUN

TODAY I AM FEELING:

THE WEATHER TODAY WAS:

TODAY I AM GRATEFUL FOR:

TO-DO LIST

MY FAVORITE PART OF TODAY WAS:

WHAT I ATE TODAY:

BREAKFAST	LUNCH	DINNER

NOTES:

DON'T FORGET!

DAILY INSPIRATION:

"I'm not afraid of storms, for I'm learning how to sail my ship."

-LOUISA MAY ALCOTT

PRODUCTIVITY SCORE FOR TODAY:

1 2 3 4 5 6 7 8 9 10

Enjoy Today

TODAY IS A GOOD DAY TO:

DATE: ____ / ____ / ____

MON TUE WED THU FRI SAT SUN

TODAY I AM FEELING:

THE WEATHER TODAY WAS:

TODAY I AM GRATEFUL FOR:

TO-DO LIST

MY FAVORITE PART OF TODAY WAS:

WHAT I ATE TODAY:

BREAKFAST	LUNCH	DINNER

NOTES:

DON'T FORGET!

DAILY INSPIRATION:

"Peace is always beautiful."

-WALT WHITMAN

PRODUCTIVITY SCORE FOR TODAY:

1 2 3 4 5 6 7 8 9 10

Enjoy Today

TODAY IS A GOOD DAY TO:

DATE: ____ / ____ / ____

MON TUE WED THU FRI SAT SUN

TODAY I AM FEELING:

THE WEATHER TODAY WAS:

TODAY I AM GRATEFUL FOR:

TO-DO LIST

MY FAVORITE PART OF TODAY WAS:

WHAT I ATE TODAY:

BREAKFAST	LUNCH	DINNER

NOTES:

DON'T FORGET!

DAILY INSPIRATION:

"Let us speak courteously, deal fairly, and keep ourselves armed and ready."

-THEODORE ROOSEVELT

PRODUCTIVITY SCORE FOR TODAY:

1 2 3 4 5 6 7 8 9 10

ENJOY TODAY

TODAY IS A GOOD DAY TO:

DATE: ____/____/____

MON TUE WED THU FRI SAT SUN

TODAY I AM FEELING:

THE WEATHER TODAY WAS:

TODAY I AM GRATEFUL FOR:

TO-DO LIST

MY FAVORITE PART OF TODAY WAS:

WHAT I ATE TODAY:

BREAKFAST	LUNCH	DINNER

NOTES:

DON'T FORGET!

DAILY INSPIRATION:

"In a revolution, as in a novel, the most difficult part to invent is the end."

-ALEXIS DE TOCQUEVILLE

PRODUCTIVITY SCORE FOR TODAY:

1 2 3 4 5 6 7 8 9 10

ENJOY TODAY

TODAY IS A GOOD DAY TO:

DATE: ____ / ____ / ____

MON TUE WED THU FRI SAT SUN

TODAY I AM FEELING:

THE WEATHER TODAY WAS:

TODAY I AM GRATEFUL FOR:

TO-DO LIST

MY FAVORITE PART OF TODAY WAS:

WHAT I ATE TODAY:

BREAKFAST	LUNCH	DINNER

NOTES:

DON'T FORGET!

DAILY INSPIRATION:

"We are healed of a suffering only by experiencing it to the full."

-MARCEL PROUST

PRODUCTIVITY SCORE FOR TODAY:

1 2 3 4 5 6 7 8 9 10

ENJOY TODAY

TODAY IS A GOOD DAY TO:

DATE: ____ / ____ / ____

MON TUE WED THU FRI SAT SUN

TODAY I AM FEELING:

THE WEATHER TODAY WAS:

TODAY I AM GRATEFUL FOR:

TO-DO LIST

MY FAVORITE PART OF TODAY WAS:

WHAT I ATE TODAY:

BREAKFAST	LUNCH	DINNER

NOTES:

DON'T FORGET!

DAILY INSPIRATION:

"'Tis a wise saying,
Drive on your own track."

-PLUTARCH

PRODUCTIVITY SCORE FOR TODAY:

1 2 3 4 5 6 7 8 9 10

ENJOY TODAY

TODAY IS A GOOD DAY TO:

DATE: ______ / ______ / ______

MON TUE WED THU FRI SAT SUN

TODAY I AM FEELING:

THE WEATHER TODAY WAS:

TODAY I AM GRATEFUL FOR:

TO-DO LIST

MY FAVORITE PART OF TODAY WAS:

WHAT I ATE TODAY:

BREAKFAST	LUNCH	DINNER

NOTES:

DON'T FORGET!

DAILY INSPIRATION:

"A man is literally what he thinks, his character being the complete sum of all his thoughts."

-JAMES ALLEN

PRODUCTIVITY SCORE FOR TODAY:

1 2 3 4 5 6 7 8 9 10

ENJOY TODAY

TODAY IS A GOOD DAY TO:

DATE: ______ /______ /______

MON TUE WED THU FRI SAT SUN

TODAY I AM FEELING:

THE WEATHER TODAY WAS:

TODAY I AM GRATEFUL FOR:

TO-DO LIST

MY FAVORITE PART OF TODAY WAS:

WHAT I ATE TODAY:

BREAKFAST	LUNCH	DINNER

NOTES:

DON'T FORGET!

DAILY INSPIRATION:

"Some of the words
you'll find within yourself,
the rest some power
will inspire you to say."

-HOMER

PRODUCTIVITY SCORE FOR TODAY:

1 2 3 4 5 6 7 8 9 10

ENJOY TODAY

TODAY IS A GOOD DAY TO:

DATE: ______ / ______ / ______

MON TUE WED THU FRI SAT SUN

TODAY I AM FEELING:

THE WEATHER TODAY WAS:

TODAY I AM GRATEFUL FOR:

TO-DO LIST

MY FAVORITE PART OF TODAY WAS:

WHAT I ATE TODAY:

BREAKFAST	LUNCH	DINNER

NOTES:

DON'T FORGET!

DAILY INSPIRATION:

"Whatever can be done another day can be done today."

-MICHEL DE MONTAIGNE

PRODUCTIVITY SCORE FOR TODAY:

1 2 3 4 5 6 7 8 9 10

ENJOY TODAY

TODAY IS A GOOD DAY TO:

DATE: ____ / ____ / ____

MON TUE WED THU FRI SAT SUN

TODAY I AM FEELING:

THE WEATHER TODAY WAS:

TODAY I AM GRATEFUL FOR:

TO-DO LIST

MY FAVORITE PART OF TODAY WAS:

WHAT I ATE TODAY:

BREAKFAST	LUNCH	DINNER

NOTES:

DON'T FORGET!

DAILY INSPIRATION:

"You cannot escape necessities, but you can overcome them."

-LUCIUS ANNAEUS SENECA

PRODUCTIVITY SCORE FOR TODAY:

1 2 3 4 5 6 7 8 9 10

ENJOY TODAY

TODAY IS A GOOD DAY TO:

DATE: ____ / ____ / ____

MON TUE WED THU FRI SAT SUN

TODAY I AM FEELING:

THE WEATHER TODAY WAS:

TODAY I AM GRATEFUL FOR:

TO-DO LIST

MY FAVORITE PART OF TODAY WAS:

WHAT I ATE TODAY:

BREAKFAST	LUNCH	DINNER

NOTES:

DON'T FORGET!

DAILY INSPIRATION:

"Act the part and you will become the part."

-WILLIAM JAMES

PRODUCTIVITY SCORE FOR TODAY:

1 2 3 4 5 6 7 8 9 10

ENJOY TODAY

TODAY IS A GOOD DAY TO:

DATE: ____ / ____ / ____

MON TUE WED THU FRI SAT SUN

TODAY I AM FEELING:

THE WEATHER TODAY WAS:

TODAY I AM GRATEFUL FOR:

TO-DO LIST

MY FAVORITE PART OF TODAY WAS:

WHAT I ATE TODAY:

BREAKFAST	LUNCH	DINNER

NOTES:

DON'T FORGET!

DAILY INSPIRATION:

"The vocation of every man and woman is to serve other people."

-LEO TOLSTOY

PRODUCTIVITY SCORE FOR TODAY:

1 2 3 4 5 6 7 8 9 10

ENJOY TODAY

TODAY IS A GOOD DAY TO:

DATE: ____/____/____

MON TUE WED THU FRI SAT SUN

TODAY I AM FEELING:

THE WEATHER TODAY WAS:

TODAY I AM GRATEFUL FOR:

TO-DO LIST

MY FAVORITE PART OF TODAY WAS:

WHAT I ATE TODAY:

BREAKFAST	LUNCH	DINNER

NOTES:

DON'T FORGET!

DAILY INSPIRATION:

"In all things of nature there is something of the marvelous."

-ARISTOTLE

PRODUCTIVITY SCORE FOR TODAY:

1 2 3 4 5 6 7 8 9 10

ENJOY TODAY

TODAY IS A GOOD DAY TO:

DATE: ____ / ____ / ____

MON TUE WED THU FRI SAT SUN

TODAY I AM FEELING:

THE WEATHER TODAY WAS:

TODAY I AM GRATEFUL FOR:

TO-DO LIST

MY FAVORITE PART OF TODAY WAS:

WHAT I ATE TODAY:

BREAKFAST	LUNCH	DINNER

NOTES:

DON'T FORGET!

DAILY INSPIRATION:

"No one is so old as to think that he cannot live one more year."

-MARCUS TULLIUS CICERO

PRODUCTIVITY SCORE FOR TODAY:

1 2 3 4 5 6 7 8 9 10

ENJOY TODAY

TODAY IS A GOOD DAY TO:

DATE: ____ / ____ / ____

MON TUE WED THU FRI SAT SUN

TODAY I AM FEELING:

THE WEATHER TODAY WAS:

TODAY I AM GRATEFUL FOR:

TO-DO LIST

MY FAVORITE PART OF TODAY WAS:

WHAT I ATE TODAY:

BREAKFAST	LUNCH	DINNER

NOTES:

DON'T FORGET!

DAILY INSPIRATION:

"The secret of being a bore is to tell everything."

-VOLTAIRE

PRODUCTIVITY SCORE FOR TODAY:

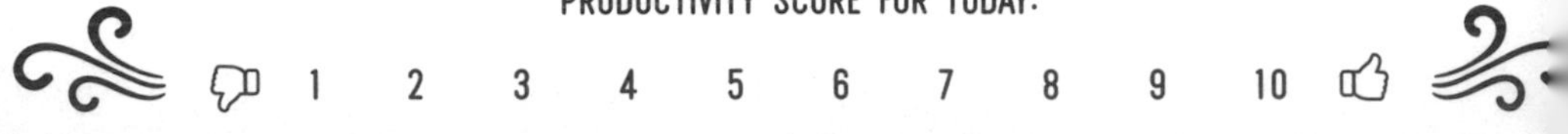

ENJOY TODAY

TODAY IS A GOOD DAY TO:

DATE: ______ / ______ / ______

MON TUE WED THU FRI SAT SUN

TODAY I AM FEELING:

THE WEATHER TODAY WAS:

TODAY I AM GRATEFUL FOR:

TO-DO LIST

MY FAVORITE PART OF TODAY WAS:

WHAT I ATE TODAY:

BREAKFAST	LUNCH	DINNER

NOTES:

DON'T FORGET!

DAILY INSPIRATION:

"Knowledge is power."

-FRANCIS BACON

PRODUCTIVITY SCORE FOR TODAY:

1 2 3 4 5 6 7 8 9 10

ENJOY TODAY

TODAY IS A GOOD DAY TO:

DATE: ____/____/____

MON TUE WED THU FRI SAT SUN

TODAY I AM FEELING:

THE WEATHER TODAY WAS:

TODAY I AM GRATEFUL FOR:

TO-DO LIST

MY FAVORITE PART OF TODAY WAS:

WHAT I ATE TODAY:

BREAKFAST	LUNCH	DINNER

NOTES:

DON'T FORGET!

DAILY INSPIRATION:

"A good heart is better than all the heads in the world."

-EDWARD BULWER-LYTTON

PRODUCTIVITY SCORE FOR TODAY:

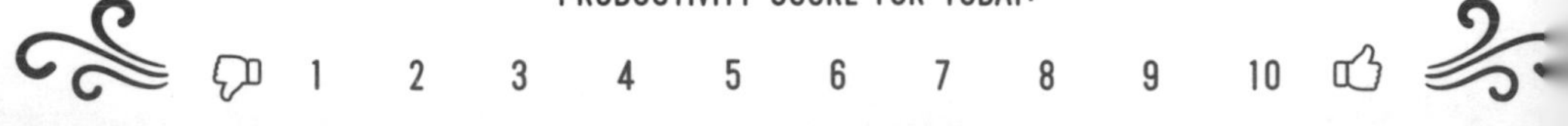

Enjoy Today

TODAY IS A GOOD DAY TO:

DATE: ____ / ____ / ____

MON TUE WED THU FRI SAT SUN

TODAY I AM FEELING:

THE WEATHER TODAY WAS:

TODAY I AM GRATEFUL FOR:

TO-DO LIST

MY FAVORITE PART OF TODAY WAS:

WHAT I ATE TODAY:

BREAKFAST	LUNCH	DINNER

NOTES:

DON'T FORGET!

DAILY INSPIRATION:

"Live as you would have wished to live when you are dying."

—CHRISTIAN FÜRCHTEGOTT GELLERT

PRODUCTIVITY SCORE FOR TODAY:

1 2 3 4 5 6 7 8 9 10

ENJOY TODAY

TODAY IS A GOOD DAY TO:

DATE: ____ / ____ / ____

MON TUE WED THU FRI SAT SUN

TODAY I AM FEELING:

THE WEATHER TODAY WAS:

TODAY I AM GRATEFUL FOR:

TO-DO LIST

MY FAVORITE PART OF TODAY WAS:

WHAT I ATE TODAY:

BREAKFAST	LUNCH	DINNER

NOTES:

DON'T FORGET!

DAILY INSPIRATION:

"Restlessness and discontent are the first necessities of progress."

-THOMAS ALVA EDISON

PRODUCTIVITY SCORE FOR TODAY:

1 2 3 4 5 6 7 8 9 10

ENJOY TODAY

TODAY IS A GOOD DAY TO:

DATE: ____ / ____ / ____

MON TUE WED THU FRI SAT SUN

TODAY I AM FEELING:

THE WEATHER TODAY WAS:

TODAY I AM GRATEFUL FOR:

TO-DO LIST

MY FAVORITE PART OF TODAY WAS:

WHAT I ATE TODAY:

BREAKFAST	LUNCH	DINNER

NOTES:

DON'T FORGET!

DAILY INSPIRATION:

"A fresh mind keeps the body fresh."

-EDWARD BULWER-LYTTON

PRODUCTIVITY SCORE FOR TODAY:

1 2 3 4 5 6 7 8 9 10

ENJOY TODAY

TODAY IS A GOOD DAY TO:

DATE: ____ / ____ / ____

MON TUE WED THU FRI SAT SUN

TODAY I AM FEELING:

THE WEATHER TODAY WAS:

TODAY I AM GRATEFUL FOR:

TO-DO LIST

MY FAVORITE PART OF TODAY WAS:

WHAT I ATE TODAY:

BREAKFAST	LUNCH	DINNER

NOTES:

DON'T FORGET!

DAILY INSPIRATION:

"Every man is the architect of his own fortune."

-GAIUS SALLUSTIUS CRISPUS

PRODUCTIVITY SCORE FOR TODAY:

1 2 3 4 5 6 7 8 9 10

ENJOY TODAY

TODAY IS A GOOD DAY TO:

DATE: ____ / ____ / ____

MON TUE WED THU FRI SAT SUN

TODAY I AM FEELING:

THE WEATHER TODAY WAS:

TODAY I AM GRATEFUL FOR:

TO-DO LIST

MY FAVORITE PART OF TODAY WAS:

WHAT I ATE TODAY:

BREAKFAST	LUNCH	DINNER

NOTES:

DON'T FORGET!

DAILY INSPIRATION:

"Variety is the soul of pleasure."

-APHRA BEHN

PRODUCTIVITY SCORE FOR TODAY:

1 2 3 4 5 6 7 8 9 10

Enjoy Today

TODAY IS A GOOD DAY TO:

DATE: ____ / ____ / ____

MON TUE WED THU FRI SAT SUN

TODAY I AM FEELING:

THE WEATHER TODAY WAS:

TODAY I AM GRATEFUL FOR:

TO-DO LIST

MY FAVORITE PART OF TODAY WAS:

WHAT I ATE TODAY:

BREAKFAST	LUNCH	DINNER

NOTES:

DON'T FORGET!

DAILY INSPIRATION:

"The most important trip you take in life is meeting people halfway."

-HENRY BOYLE

PRODUCTIVITY SCORE FOR TODAY:

1 2 3 4 5 6 7 8 9 10

Enjoy Today

TODAY IS A GOOD DAY TO:

DATE: ______ / ______ / ______

MON TUE WED THU FRI SAT SUN

TODAY I AM FEELING:

THE WEATHER TODAY WAS:

TODAY I AM GRATEFUL FOR:

TO-DO LIST

MY FAVORITE PART OF TODAY WAS:

WHAT I ATE TODAY:

BREAKFAST	LUNCH	DINNER

NOTES:

DON'T FORGET!

DAILY INSPIRATION:

"A good conscience is a continual feast."

-ROBERT BURTON

PRODUCTIVITY SCORE FOR TODAY:

1 2 3 4 5 6 7 8 9 10

ENJOY TODAY

TODAY IS A GOOD DAY TO:

DATE: ____/____/____

MON TUE WED THU FRI SAT SUN

TODAY I AM FEELING:

THE WEATHER TODAY WAS:

TODAY I AM GRATEFUL FOR:

TO-DO LIST

MY FAVORITE PART OF TODAY WAS:

WHAT I ATE TODAY:

BREAKFAST	LUNCH	DINNER

NOTES:

DON'T FORGET!

DAILY INSPIRATION:

"Everything changes and nothing stands still."

-HERACLITUS

PRODUCTIVITY SCORE FOR TODAY:

1 2 3 4 5 6 7 8 9 10

ENJOY TODAY

TODAY IS A GOOD DAY TO:

DATE: ____ / ____ / ____

MON TUE WED THU FRI SAT SUN

TODAY I AM FEELING:

THE WEATHER TODAY WAS:

TODAY I AM GRATEFUL FOR:

TO-DO LIST

MY FAVORITE PART OF TODAY WAS:

WHAT I ATE TODAY:

BREAKFAST	LUNCH	DINNER

NOTES:

DON'T FORGET!

DAILY INSPIRATION:

"Self-sufficiency is the greatest of all wealth."

-EPICURUS

PRODUCTIVITY SCORE FOR TODAY:

1 2 3 4 5 6 7 8 9 10

ENJOY TODAY

TODAY IS A GOOD DAY TO:

DATE: ____ / ____ / ____

MON TUE WED THU FRI SAT SUN

TODAY I AM FEELING:

THE WEATHER TODAY WAS:

TODAY I AM GRATEFUL FOR:

TO-DO LIST

MY FAVORITE PART OF TODAY WAS:

WHAT I ATE TODAY:

BREAKFAST	LUNCH	DINNER

NOTES:

DON'T FORGET!

DAILY INSPIRATION:

"Love is a great beautifier."

-LOUISA MAY ALCOTT

PRODUCTIVITY SCORE FOR TODAY:

1 2 3 4 5 6 7 8 9 10

Looking for more?

Similar titles available by piccadilly:

300 Writing Prompts

300 More Writing Prompts

500 Writing Prompts

3000 Questions About Me

3000 Would You Rather Questions

Choose Your Own Journal

Complete The Story

Your Father's Story

Your Mother's Story

The Story Of My Life

Write The Story

300 Drawing Prompts

500 Drawing Prompts

Calligraphy Made Easy

Comic Sketchbook

Sketching Made Easy

100 Life Challenges

Awesome Social Media Quizzes

Find The Cat

Find 2 Cats

Time Capsule Letters